Emma.

Miss Emma E Allen

Guthrie
O.T.

Emma E. Allen
Guthrie
Ind.

Friend ship is the golden
link that bindes us heart
to heart and near one link
of it shall break when true
friends haft to part

The few lines to you are India[?]
From a Friend once and true
Hoping [always?] try to be remembered
when I am far away from you
your Friend
[signature]

WORDSWORTH   SCOTT

SHAKESPEARE

TENNYSON   GOLDSMITH

INDIANA STATE SERIES

FIFTH READER

REVISED BY

S. H. CLARK, Ph.B.

THE UNIVERSITY OF CHICAGO

IN COLLABORATION WITH

H. S. FISKE, A.M.

THE UNIVERSITY OF CHICAGO

INDIANAPOLIS, IND.

INDIANA SCHOOL BOOK CO.

INTRODUCTION

In choosing material for reading books to be used by pupils who have already acquired some facility in recognizing word forms, the purposes of the reading lesson must be clearly apprehended. These seem to be three: first, to inculcate a love for what is best and highest in literature; second, to train the child in correct habits of thought getting from the printed page; and, third, to train him in vocal expression.

If this statement of the purposes of the reading lesson is true, it must be evident that selections of a purely scientific character, and others that may be included under the general head of "information literature," should find small space in our readers. In these days, when every schoolroom is supplied with supplementary reading, there is no dearth of information material; and, therefore, it appears unfair to the child to insert very much of such material when space might be used to much greater advantage to supply him with selections that are more essentially literary. Again, early scientific training does not consist in reading about the facts of nature, but in coming into direct contact with them. Hence, the training in science should be of a practical kind, and not that derived from the perusal of facts set down on the printed page.

The scientific matter found in the third, fourth, and fifth readers of this series is inserted to afford the teacher an opportunity to train the pupils in the manner of using such selections, rather than to develop vocal expression. Every sentence should be carefully scanned, every statement made as concrete as possible by means of drawing, illustration, and the presentation of actual objects, and the class should be held responsible for the mastery of the facts, and not for definitions or repetition of phrases, the true meaning of which they have not grasped. By this method the necessity of the utmost care in the preparation of such lessons is impressed upon the class, to the great advantage of future supplementary reading in science and history.

Selections of an historical nature find a larger place in these readers. While this class of material may generally be included under the head of "information literature," it serves yet another purpose besides that of giving facts. It is here inserted mainly for its intrinsic interest. It is vital, direct, and especially stimulating to the imagination. Together with the scientific selections it will be found to afford excellent practice in training the pupil in careful and discriminating thought getting.

Much time and careful study have been devoted to choosing and arranging the selections. It should be helpful to the teacher to understand the principles that have guided in this choice and arrangement.

In the first place, and especially in the third and fourth readers, *subjective, introspective, reflective, literature has been almost entirely eliminated.* Young children have not had the experience to appreciate the spirit of such literature, and, therefore, the selections chosen are *objective, vital, and of intrinsic interest.*

This principle of selection having been settled upon, the next test naturally applied was, *Is the selection good literature for the children for whom it is chosen?* It is not to be forgotten that literature which is too far beyond the child may be, in its confusing and discouraging effect, as harmful as matter without vital interest or literary form.

These questions answered, the next point for consideration was *whether the literary style is sufficiently simple not to interfere with the child's pleasure in reading.* Perhaps the method of selection may best be shown by illustration. Longfellow's *Bell of Atri* is, as a whole, simple in spirit, and the story, told in prose, of great interest even to very young children; but the style is far beyond them. The suspended sense and the subordinate clauses of the opening paragraph render the reading of the lines so difficult that the results from teaching them would hardly justify the teacher's effort. If the spirit of a selection is within the grasp of the child, and the selection is of high literary merit and contains but one or two difficult sentences, it may justly find a place notwithstanding the difficulties; but where rhetorical obstacles are too frequent, it is deemed advisable to omit the selection altogether or to insert it later on. It would be well to bear this statement in mind when the teacher discovers apparently simple selections in the later portions of the book.

It is also to be noted, that this same principle determines the place of material the style of which is simple, but the spirit of which is beyond the average child. *The Day is Done*, by Longfellow, is an example of this class of selections. The style is artistically simple, but the spirit is far beyond the young child. Reading this selection casually the adult will be very likely, especially if he is desirous of choosing good literature for children, to insert this poem in the fourth, and perhaps even in the third, reader. But what child of eleven or twelve years has felt coming over him the sadness that is not akin to pain? And how, therefore, can he appreciate the *effect* of the soothing melody that the poet craves to hear? What does he know of the cares that infest the day, in the sense in which Longfellow uses the words? It is true, we may teach the superficial meaning of the words (and herein lies the danger), but anything approximating a true interpretation of the poem is hardly possible for young children. It may be said again, if the spirit of only one or two stanzas of a poem is beyond the child, it would be well to insert it notwithstanding. But we must be careful to distinguish between poems of such a character and a poem like *The Day is Done*.

The lines descriptive of the churchyard, in *Paul Revere's Ride*, are beyond the experience of the average third or fourth grade child; and yet, since the poem as a whole is by no means difficult, is good literature, and particularly interesting, we may pass over the one difficult passage and return to it, if need be, at some future time. Such a course is preferable to omitting the difficult passage altogether.

The chief use of the reader is that it may serve as an introduction to the study of literature. The great majority of our children will never come into direct contact with any art but literature. They will never see great paintings and sculpture, and never hear great music adequately rendered. But what is best in English literature is within the reach of all. It is, then, the duty of our educational system to create a taste for what is best by putting the best into the hands of children, and training them to enjoy it — not for the information it conveys, but for its influence upon their culture and their spiritual well-being.

The notes in this series serve chiefly two ends : to explain certain unusual terms and allusions, and to assist the teacher in bringing out the literary beauty and strength. Too much stress cannot be laid upon the proper use of these notes, which are intended not so much for the class as for the teacher. The utmost care must be observed not to turn poetry into prose. It is not so much the meaning of a line as its poetic significance that the child must grasp. Further, we must remember that the true definition of a word is not another word, but a picture. By keeping this in mind we may do much not only to enhance the child's pleasure, but to increase his vocabulary and power of expression. Lastly, let the teacher thoroughly master every selection before teaching it. If a selection contains many difficulties, it is well to clear these away, whenever possible, before even announcing the lesson. Mythological, historical, and scientific allusions and references may easily be brought in at almost any time during the day; the new words may be used by the teacher in the course of any lesson; and so, by the time the reading lesson comes, many obstacles may have been removed. Particular attention of all teachers is called to the notes on *Abou Ben Adhem* and the *Daffodils* in the third reader.

Within the narrow limits of an introductory chapter it is impossible to cover the wide field of vocal expression. Although the development of literary taste, with all that term implies, is the primary object of the reading lesson, we may not overlook the expressive side of reading. The teacher, therefore, should give special care to the oral expression, endeavoring to have it natural and, above all, full of meaning and appropriate feeling.

CONTENTS

PAGE

Kentucky Belle . . .	Constance Fenimore Woolson	11
The First Grenadier of France	. . . . .	19
Young Lochinvar . .	. . . Walter Scott	25
Little and Great . .	. . . Charles Mackay	27
The Farmer and the Fox	. . James Anthony Froude	29
The Soldier's Dream .	. . . Thomas Campbell	31
The Heights of Abraham	. . . Francis Parkman	32
Maud Muller . . .	. John Greenleaf Whittier	44
Story of Alnaschar .	. . . Joseph Addison	49
The Blue and the Gray .	. . Francis Miles Finch	52
The Destruction of Sennacherib	. . . Lord Byron	54
A Ruffian in Feathers .	. . . Olive Thorne Miller	55
The Rising in 1776 .	. . Thomas Buchanan Read	60
Eskimo Dog Teams .	. . . Elisha Kent Kane	65
An Order for a Picture .	. . . . Alice Cary	68
The Land of Souls .	. . Henry R. Schoolcraft	73
Gradatim . . .	. . Josiah Gilbert Holland	78
Under the Greenwood Tree .	. . William Shakespeare	79
The Sagacity of the Spider .	. . Oliver Goldsmith	80
Perseverance . . .	. . . . .	85
To Daffodils . .	. . . . Robert Herrick	86
Horseshoe Robinson's Ruse .	. . John P. Kennedy	87
Arnold Von Winkelried	. . . James Montgomery	100
The Spaniards' Retreat from Mexico	. W. H. Prescott	103
Concord Hymn . .	. . R. W. Emerson	113
One Niche the Highest .	. . . . Elihu Burritt	114
The School at Dotheboys Hall	. . Charles Dickens	118
The Burial of Moses .	. Mrs. Cecil Frances Alexander	128
The Discovery of the Mississippi .	. George Bancroft	132
Song of the Chattahoochee .	. . . Sidney Lanier	139
John Bull and Brother Jonathan .	James Kirke Paulding	141
The Building of the Ship .	Henry Wadsworth Longfellow	145
Julius Cæsar . .	. . . James Anthony Froude	153
A Psalm of Life . .	. Henry Wadsworth Longfellow	156

10 CONTENTS

PAGE

Union and Liberty . . . *Oliver Wendell Holmes* 158
The Eagle's Nest . . . . . . *John Wilson* 159
Ring Out, Wild Bells . . . . *Alfred Tennyson* 167
The Solitary Reaper . . . *William Wordsworth* 169
The Character of Washington . . *Thomas Jefferson* 171
Fitz-James and Roderick Dhu . . . *Walter Scott* 173
A Visit to Niagara . . . *Charles Dudley Warner* 181
Battle Hymn of the Republic . . *Julia Ward Howe* 192
O Captain! My Captain! . . . . *Walt Whitman* 193
Speech on a Resolution to put Virginia into a State of De-
fense . . . . . . *Patrick Henry* 195
Life . . . . . . *Anna Letitia Barbauld* 199
The Day is Done . . . *Henry Wadsworth Longfellow* 200
Rab and his Friends . . . . *Dr. John Brown* 202
The Poetry of Earth is Never Dead . . *John Keats* 221
The Crowded Street . . . *William Cullen Bryant* 221
Among the Icebergs . . . . . *Isaac I. Hayes* 223
The Arsenal at Springfield . *Henry Wadsworth Longfellow* 231
The Shell . . . . . . *Alfred Tennyson* 233
In Favor of Independence . . . *Daniel Webster* 234
The Revenge . . . . . . *Alfred Tennyson* 239
Duty's Leaden Casket . . . *James Russell Lowell* 246
The Battle of Waterloo . . . . . *Victor Hugo* 247
The Village Preacher . . . . *Oliver Goldsmith* 259
To a Water-Fowl . . . . *William Cullen Bryant* 261
The Story of Ruth . . . . . . *The Bible* 262
The Forum Scene from Julius Cæsar *William Shakespeare* 272
Rip Van Winkle . . . . . *Washington Irving* 283
The Chambered Nautilus . . *Oliver Wendell Holmes* 307
The Light of Stars . . *Henry Wadsworth Longfellow* 308
Second Inaugural Address . . . *Abraham Lincoln* 310
King Henry's Address to his Soldiers *William Shakespeare* 313
Elegy written in a Country Churchyard . *Thomas Gray* 314
Scenery of the Yosemite Valley . . *Thomas Starr King* 319
Thanatopsis . . . . . *William Cullen Bryant* 325
Crossing the Bar . . . . . *Alfred Tennyson* 328

Notes 329

FIFTH READER

KENTUCKY BELLE

Constance Fenimore Woolson

Summer of 'sixty-three, and Conrad was gone away —
Gone to the country town, sir, to sell our first load of
    hay :
We lived in the log house yonder, poor as ever you've
    seen ;
Röschen there was a baby, and I was only nineteen.

Conrad he took the oxen, but he left Kentucky Belle.
How much we thought of Kentuck, I couldn't begin
    to tell —
Came from the Blue-grass country ; my father gave
    her to me
When I rode north with Conrad, away from the
    Tennessee.

Conrad lived in Ohio — a German he is, you know.
The house stood in broad cornfields, stretching on, row
    after row.

The old folks made me welcome ; they were kind as
    kind could be ;
But I kept longing, longing, for the hills of the
    Tennessee.

Oh for a sight of water, the shadowed slope of a hill !
Clouds that hang on the summit, a wind that never is
    still !
But the level land went stretching away to meet the
    sky —
Never a rise from north to south, to rest the weary eye !

From east to west, no river to shine out under the moon,
Nothing to make a shadow in the yellow afternoon :
Only the breathless sunshine, as I looked out, all for-
    lorn ;
Only the "rustle, rustle," as I walked among the corn.

When I fell sick with pining, we didn't wait any
    more,
But moved away from the corn lands, out to this river
    shore —
The Tuscarawas it's called, sir — off there's a hill, you
    see —
And now I've grown to like it next best to the Tennessee.

I was at work that morning. Some one came riding
    like mad
Over the bridge and up the road — Farmer Routh's
    little lad.

Bareback he rode; he had no hat; he hardly stopped
    to say:
" Morgan's men are coming, Frau; they're galloping
    on this way.

" I'm sent to warn the neighbors. He isn't a mile
    behind ;
He sweeps up all the horses — every horse that he can
    find.
Morgan, Morgan the raider, and Morgan's terrible
    men,
With bowie knives and pistols, are galloping up the
    glen ! "

The lad rode down the valley, and I stood still at the
    door ;
The baby laughed and prattled, playing with spools
    on the floor ;
Kentuck was out in the pasture ; Conrad, my man, was
    gone.
Near, nearer, Morgan's men were galloping, galloping
    on !

Sudden I picked up baby, and ran to the pasture bar.
" Kentuck ! " I called — " Kentucky ! " She knew me
    ever so far !
I led her down the gully that turns off there to the
    right,
And tied her to the bushes ; her head was just out of
    sight.

As I ran back to the log house, at once there came a
    sound —
The ring of hoofs, galloping hoofs, trembling over the
    ground —
Coming into the turnpike out from the White-woman
    Glen —
Morgan, Morgan the raider, and Morgan's terrible men.

As near they drew and nearer, my heart beat fast in
    alarm ;
But still I stood in the doorway with baby on my arm.
They came ; they passed ; with spur and whip in haste
    they sped along —
Morgan, Morgan the raider, and his band, six hundred
    strong.

Weary they looked and jaded, riding through night
    and through day ;
Pushing on east to the river, many long miles away,
To the border-strip where Virginia runs up into the
    west,
And fording the upper Ohio before they could stop to
    rest.

On like the wind they hurried, and Morgan rode in
    advance ;
Bright were his eyes like live coals, as he gave me a
    sidewise glance ;
And I was just breathing freely, after my choking pain,
When the last one of the troopers suddenly drew his
    rein.

Frightened I was to death, sir; I scarce dared look in
    his face,
As he asked for a drink of water, and glanced around
    the place.
I gave him a cup, and he smiled — 'twas only a boy,
    you see,
Faint and worn, with dim blue eyes; and he'd sailed
    on the Tennessee.

Only sixteen he was, sir — a fond mother's only
    son —
Off and away with Morgan before his life had begun;
The damp drops stood on his temples; drawn was the
    boyish mouth;
And I thought me of the mother waiting down in the
    South.

Oh! pluck was he to the backbone, and clear grit
    through and through;
Boasted and bragged like a trooper; but the big words
    wouldn't do; —
The boy was dying, sir, dying, as plain as plain could
    be,
Worn out by his ride with Morgan up from the Ten-
    nessee.

But when I told the laddie that I too was from the
    South,
Water came in his dim eyes, and quivers around his
    mouth.

"Do you know the Blue-grass country?" he wistful
    began to say;
Then swayed like a willow sapling, and fainted dead
    away.

I had him into the log house, and worked and brought
    him to;
I fed him, and I coaxed him, as I thought his mother'd
    do;
And when the lad got better, and the noise in his head
    was gone,
Morgan's men were miles away, galloping, galloping
    on.

"Oh, I must go!" he muttered; "I must be up and
    away!
Morgan — Morgan is waiting for me!   Oh, what will
    Morgan say?"
But I heard a sound of tramping, and kept him back
    from the door —
The ringing sound of horses' hoofs that I had heard
    before.

And on, on came the soldiers—the Michigan cavalry—
And fast they rode, and black they looked, galloping
    rapidly:
They had followed hard on Morgan's track; they had
    followed day and night;
But of Morgan and Morgan's raiders they had never
    caught a sight.

And rich Ohio sat startled through all those summer
    days ;
For strange, wild men were galloping over her broad
    highways —
Now here, now there, now seen, now gone, now north,
    now east, now west,
Through river valleys and corn land farms, sweeping
    away her best.

A bold ride and a long ride ! But they were taken at
    last.
They almost reached the river by galloping hard and
    fast ;
But the boys in blue were upon them ere ever they
    gained the ford,
And Morgan, Morgan the raider, laid down his terrible
    sword.

Well, I kept the boy till evening — kept him against
    his will —
But he was too weak to follow, and sat there pale and
    still.
When it was cool and dusky — you'll wonder to hear
    me tell,
But I stole down to that gully and brought up Ken-
    tucky Belle.

I kissed the star on her forehead — my pretty, gentle
    lass —
But I knew that she'd be happy back in the old Blue-
    grass.

A suit of clothes of Conrad's with all the money I had,
And Kentuck, pretty Kentuck, I gave to the worn-out
    lad.

I guided him to the southward as well as I knew
    how ;
The boy rode off with many thanks and many a back-
    ward bow ;
And then the glow it faded, and my heart began to
    swell,
As down the glen away she went, my lost Kentucky
    Belle !

When Conrad came in the evening, the moon was
    shining high ;
Baby and I were both crying — I couldn't tell him
    why —
But a battered suit of rebel gray was hanging on the
    wall,
And a thin old horse, with drooping head, stood in
    Kentucky's stall.

Well, he was kind, and never once said a hard word to
    me ;
He knew I couldn't help it — 'twas all for the Ten-
    nessee.
But, after the war was over, just think what came to
    pass —
A letter, sir ; and the two were safe back in the old
    Blue-grass.

The lad had got across the border, riding Kentucky
    Belle ;
And Kentuck she was thriving, and fat, and hearty,
    and well ;
He cared for her, and kept her, nor touched her with
    whip or spur.
Ah! we've had many horses since, but never a horse
    like her !

THE FIRST GRENADIER OF FRANCE

For many years a touching and beautiful custom
might have been witnessed in a certain regiment of
French grenadiers, which was meant to commemorate
the heroism of a departed comrade. When the companies assembled for parade and the roll was called,
there was one name to which its owner could not answer — it was that of La Tour d'Auvergne. When it
was called, the oldest sergeant present stepped a pace
forward, and, raising his hand to his cap, said proudly :
" Died on the field of honor."

He was not unworthy in life of the honor thus paid
him after his death. He was educated for the army,
which he entered in 1767. He always served with dis-
tinction, but he constantly refused offers of promotion,
saying that he was only fit for the command of a company of grenadiers ; but, finally, the various grenadier
companies being united, he found himself in command
of a body of eight thousand men, while retaining only

the rank of captain. Hence he was known as "The First Grenadier of France."

When he was forty years of age, he went on a visit to a friend, in a region that was soon to become the scene of a campaign. While there, he was careful to acquaint himself with the country, thinking it not unlikely that this knowledge might be of use to him. He presently learned that the war had actually shifted to that quarter.

A regiment of Austrians was pushing on to occupy a narrow pass, the possession of which would give them an opportunity to prevent an important movement of the French which was then in progress. They hoped to surprise this post, and were moving so rapidly upon it that they were not more than two hours' distant from the place where the grenadier was staying, and which they would have to pass in their march.

He had no idea of being captured by the enemy in their advance, and he at once set off for the pass. He knew that it was defended by a stout tower and a garrison of thirty men, and he hoped to be able to warn the French of their danger.

He hastened on, and, arriving there, found the tower in a perfect condition. But it had just been vacated by the garrison, who, hearing of the approach of the Austrians, had fled, leaving their arms, consisting of thirty excellent muskets.

He gnashed his teeth with rage when he discovered this. Searching in the building, he found several boxes of ammunition which the cowards had not destroyed.

For a moment he was in despair ; but immediately, with a grim smile, he began to fasten the main door and pile against it such articles as he could find.

When he had done this, he loaded all the guns, and placed them, together with a good supply of ammunition, under the loopholes that commanded the road by which the enemy must advance. Then he ate heartily of the provisions he had brought with him, and sat down to wait. He had formed the heroic resolution to defend the tower alone against the enemy. There were some things in his favor in such an undertaking.

The pass was steep and narrow, and the enemy's troops could enter it only in double files, in doing which they would be fully exposed to the fire from the tower. The garrison of thirty men could easily have held it against a division, and now one man was about to hold it against a regiment.

It was dark when he reached the tower, and he had to wait some time for the enemy. They were longer in coming than he expected, and for a while he was tempted to believe that they had abandoned the expedition.

About midnight, however, his practiced ear caught the tramp of feet. Every moment they came nearer, and at last he heard them entering the defile. He immediately discharged two muskets into the darkness, to warn the enemy that he knew of their presence and intention ; then he heard the quick, short commands of the officer, and, from the sounds, supposed that the troops were retiring from the pass.

Until morning he was undisturbed. The Austrian

commander, feeling assured that the garrison had been informed of his movements, and was prepared to receive him, saw that he could not surprise the post as he had hoped to do, and deemed it prudent to wait till daylight before making his attack.

At sunrise, the Austrian commander called on the garrison to surrender. A grenadier answered the summons. " Say to your commander," he said, in reply to the messenger, " that the garrison will defend this pass to the last extremity."

The officer who had borne the flag of truce retired, and in about ten minutes a piece of artillery was brought into the pass. In order to bear upon the tower, it had to be placed directly in front, and within easy musket range of it. Scarcely was it got into position when a rapid fire was opened on it from the tower; and this was continued with such marked effect that the gun was withdrawn after the second discharge, with a loss of five men.

This was a bad beginning; so, half an hour after the gun was withdrawn, the Austrian colonel ordered an assault.

As the troops entered the defile, they were received with so rapid and accurate a fire, that, when they had passed over half the distance they had to traverse, they had lost fifteen men. Disheartened by this, they returned to the mouth of the pass.

Three more assaults were repulsed in this manner, and the enemy by sunset had lost forty-five men, of whom ten were killed.

The firing from the tower had been rapid and accurate, but the Austrian commander noticed this peculiarity about it — every shot seemed to come from the same place. For a while this perplexed him, but at last he came to the conclusion that there were a number of loopholes close together in the tower, so constructed as to command the ravine perfectly.

At sunset the last assault was made and repulsed, and at dark the Austrian commander sent a second summons to the garrison.

This time the answer was favorable. The garrison offered to surrender at sunrise next morning, if allowed to march out with their arms and return to the army unmolested. After some hesitation the terms were accepted.

Meantime the French soldier had passed an anxious day in the tower. He had opened the fight with thirty loaded muskets, but had not been able to discharge them all. He had fired with great rapidity, yet with surprising accuracy — for it was well known in the army that he never threw away a shot.

He had determined to stand to his post until he had accomplished his object, which was to hold the place twenty-four hours, in order to give the French army time to complete its maneuver. After that he knew the pass would be of no consequence to the enemy.

The next day at sunrise the Austrian troops lined the pass in two files, extending from the mouth of the ravine to the tower, leaving a space between them for the garrison to pass out.

And now am I come, with this lost love of mine,
To lead but one measure, drink one cup of wine.
There are maidens in Scotland more lovely by far,
That would gladly be bride to the young Lochinvar."

The bride kissed the goblet ; the knight took it up,
He quaffed off the wine, and he threw down the cup.
She looked down to blush, and she looked up to sigh,
With a smile on her lips and a tear in her eye.
He took her soft hand ere her mother could bar, —
" Now tread we a measure ! " said young Lochinvar.

So stately his form, and so lovely her face,
That never a hall such a galliard did grace ;
While her mother did fret, and her father did fume,
And the bridegroom stood dangling his bonnet and
    plume ;
And the bridemaidens whispered, " 'Twere better by
    far
To have matched our fair cousin with young Lochinvar."

One touch to her hand and one word in her ear,
When they reached the hall door ; and the charger stood
    near ;
So light to the croupe the fair lady he swung,
So light to the saddle before her he sprung !
" She is won ! we are gone, over bank, bush, and scaur ;
They'll have fleet steeds that follow," quoth young
    Lochinvar.

There was mounting 'mong Græmes of the Netherby
    clan ;
Forsters, Fenwicks, and Musgraves, they rode and they
    ran :
There was racing and chasing on Cannobie Lea,
But the lost bride of Netherby ne'er did they see.
So daring in love and so dauntless in war,
Have ye e'er heard of gallant like young Lochinvar ?

LITTLE AND GREAT

Charles Mackay

A TRAVELER, through a dusty road,
    Strewed acorns on the lea ;
And one took root and sprouted up,
    And grew into a tree.
Love sought its shade at evening time,
    To breathe its early vows ;
And Age was pleased, in heats of noon,
    To bask beneath its boughs.
The dormouse loved its dangling twigs,
    The birds sweet music bore ;
It stood a glory in its place,
    A blessing evermore.

A little spring had lost its way
    Amid the grass and fern ;
A passing stranger scooped a well,
    Where weary men might turn.

thing, chose to make me," the fox answered. " I didn't make myself."

" You stole my geese," said the man.

" Why did nature make me like geese, then? " said the fox. " Live and let live; give me my share, and I won't touch yours; but you keep them all to yourself."

" I don't understand your fine talk," answered the farmer; " but I know that you are a thief, and that you deserve to be hanged."

" His head is too thick to let me catch him so; I wonder if his heart is any softer," thought the fox. " You are taking away the life of a fellow-creature," he said; " that's a responsibility, — it is a curious thing, that life, and who knows what comes after it? You say I am a rogue. I say I am not; but at any rate I ought not to be hanged, — for if I am not, I don't deserve it; and if I am, you should give me time to repent! " " I have him now," thought the fox; " let him get out if he can."

" Why, what would you have me do with you? " said the man.

" My notion is that you should let me go, and give me a lamb, or a goose or two, every month, and then I could live without stealing; but perhaps you know better than I, and I am a rogue; my education may have been neglected; you should shut me up, and take care of me, and teach me. Who knows but in the end I may turn into a dog? "

" Very pretty," said the farmer; " we have dogs

enough, and more, too, than we can take care of, without you. No, no, Master Fox; I have caught you, and you shall swing, whatever is the logic of it. There will be one rogue less in the world, anyhow."

"It is mere hate and unchristian vengeance," said the fox.

"No, friend," the farmer answered; I don't hate you, and I don't want to revenge myself on you; but you and I can't get on together, and I think I am of more importance than you. If nettles and thistles grow in my cabbage garden, I don't try to persuade them to grow into cabbages. I just dig them up. I don't hate them; but I feel somehow that they mustn't hinder me with my cabbages, and that I must put them away; and so, my poor friend, I am sorry for you, but I am afraid you must swing."

THE SOLDIER'S DREAM

Thomas Campbell

OUR bugles sang truce; for the night cloud had lowered,
   And the sentinel stars set their watch in the sky;
And thousands had sunk on the ground overpowered—
   The weary to sleep, and the wounded to die.

When reposing that night on my pallet of straw,
   By the wolf-scaring fagot that guarded the slain,
At the dead of the night a sweet vision I saw,
   And thrice ere the morning I dreamt it again.

Methought from the battlefield's dreadful array,
   Far, far I had roamed on a desolate track ;
'Twas autumn — and sunshine arose on the way
   To the home of my fathers, that welcomed me back.

I flew to the pleasant fields traversed so oft
   In life's morning march, when my bosom was young ;
I heard my own mountain goats bleating aloft,
   And knew the sweet strain that the corn-reapers
     sung.

Then pledged we the wine-cup, and fondly I swore
   From my home and my weeping friends never to
     part ;
My little ones kissed me a thousand times o'er,
   And my wife sobbed aloud in her fullness of heart.

"Stay, stay with us ! — rest ; thou art weary and
     worn ! "
   And fain was their war-broken soldier to stay ;
But sorrow returned with the dawning of morn,
   And the voice in my dreaming ear melted away !

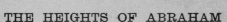

THE HEIGHTS OF ABRAHAM

Francis Parkman

For full two hours the procession of boats, borne on
the current, steered silently down the St. Lawrence.
The stars were visible, but the night was moonless and
sufficiently dark. The general was in one of the fore-

most boats, and near him was a young midshipman, John Robinson, afterwards Professor of Natural Philosophy in the University of Edinburgh. He used to tell in his later life how Wolfe, with a low voice, repeated Gray's " Elegy in a Country Churchyard " to the officers about him. Probably it was to relieve the intense strain of his thoughts. Among the rest was the verse which his own fate was soon to illustrate —

"The paths of glory lead but to the grave."

"Gentlemen," he said, as his recital ended, " I would rather have written those lines than take Quebec." None were there to tell him that the hero is greater than the poet.

As they neared their destination the tide bore them in toward the shore, and the mighty wall' of rock and forest towered in darkness on their left. The dead stillness was suddenly broken by the sharp " *Qui vive ?* " [" Who goes there ? "] of a French sentry, invisible in the thick gloom. " *France !* " answered a Highland officer of Fraser's regiment, from one of the boats of the light infantry. He had served in Holland, and spoke French fluently.

" *À quel régiment ?* " [" To what regiment ? "]

" *De la Reine,* " [" The Queen's "] replied the Highlander. He knew that a part of that corps was with Bougainville. The sentry, expecting the convoy of provisions, was satisfied, and did not ask for the password.

Soon after, the foremost boats were passing the

heights of Samos, when another sentry challenged them, and they could see him through the darkness running down to the edge of the water, within range of a pistol shot. In answer to his questions, the same officer replied in French. "Provision boats. Don't make a noise, the English will hear us." In fact, the sloop of war *Hunter* was anchored in the stream not far off. This time, again, the sentry let them pass. In a few moments they rounded the headland above the Anse du Foulon. There was no sentry there. The strong current swept the boats of the light infantry a little below the intended landing place. They disembarked on a narrow strand at the foot of heights as steep as a hill covered with trees can be. The twenty-four volunteers led the way, climbing with what silence they might, closely followed by a much larger body. When they reached the top, they saw in the dim light a cluster of tents at a short distance, and immediately made a dash at them. Vergor leaped from bed and tried to run off, but was shot in the heel and captured. His men, taken by surprise, made little resistance. One or two were caught, and the rest fled.

The main body of troops waited in their boats by the edge of the strand. The heights near by were cleft by a great ravine choked with forest trees, and in its depths ran a little brook which, swollen by the late rains, fell plashing in the stillness over a rock. Other than this no sound could reach the strained ear of Wolfe, but the gurgle of the tide and the cautious climbing of his advance parties as they mounted the

steeps at some little distance from where he sat listening. At length from the top came a sound of musket
shots, followed by loud huzzas, and he knew that his
men were masters of the position. The word was
given ; the troops leaped from the boats and scaled
the heights, some here, some there, clutching at trees
and bushes, their muskets slung at their backs. Tradition still points out the place, near the mouth of the
ravine, where the foremost reached the top. Wolfe
said to an officer near him, " You can try it, but I don't
think you'll get up." He himself, however, found
strength to drag himself up with the rest. The narrow, slanting path on the face of the heights had been
made impassable by trenches and abatis, but all ob-
structions were soon cleared away, and then the ascent
was easy. In the gray of the morning the long file of
red-coated soldiers moved quickly upward, and formed
in order on the plateau above.

Before many of them had reached the top, cannon
was heard close on the left. It was the battery at
Samos firing on the boats in the rear and the vessels
descending from Cap-Rouge. A party was sent to
silence it. This was soon effected, and the more distant battery at Sillery was next attacked and taken.
As fast as the boats were emptied they returned for
the troops left on board the vessels, and for those waiting on the southern shore under Colonel Burton.

The day broke in clouds and threatening rain.
Wolfe's battalions were drawn up along the crest of
the heights. No enemy was in sight, though a body

of Canadians had sallied from the town and moved along the strand toward the landing place, whence they were quickly driven back. He had achieved the most critical part of his enterprise, yet the success that he coveted placed him in imminent danger. On one side was the garrison of Quebec and the army of Beauport, and Bougainville was on the other. Wolfe's alternative was victory or ruin ; for if he should be overwhelmed by a combined attack, retreat would be hopeless. His feelings no man can know, but it would be safe to say that hesitation or doubt had no place in them.

He went to reconnoiter the ground, and soon came to the Plains of Abraham, so called from Abraham Martin, a pilot known as Maître Abraham, who had owned a piece of land here in the early times of the colony. The Plains were a tract of grass, tolerably level in most parts, patched here and there with cornfields, studded with clumps of bushes, and forming a part of the high plateau at the eastern end of which Quebec stood. On the south it was bounded by the declivities along the St. Lawrence ; on the north by those along the St. Charles, or rather along the meadows through which that lazy stream crawled like a writhing snake. At the place that Wolfe chose for his battle-field the plateau was less than a mile wide.

Thither the troops advanced, marched by files till they reached the ground, and then wheeled to form their line of battle, which stretched across the plateau and faced the city. It consisted of six battalions and the detached grenadiers from Louisbourg, all drawn up in ranks three deep. Its right wing was near the brink of the heights along the St. Lawrence, but the left could not reach those along the St. Charles. On this side a wide space was perforce left open, and there was danger of being outflanked. To prevent this, Brigadier Townshend was stationed here with two battalions, drawn up at right angles with the rest, and fronting the St. Charles. The battalion of Webb's regiment, under Colonel Burton, formed the reserve; the third battalion of Royal Americans was left to guard the landing; and Howe's light infantry occupied a wood far in the rear. Wolfe, with Monckton and Murray, commanded the front line, on which the heavy fighting was to fall, and which, when all the troops had arrived, numbered less than thirty-five hundred men.

Quebec was not a mile distant, but they could not see it, for a ridge of broken ground intervened about six hundred paces off. The first division of troops had scarcely come up when, about six o'clock, this ridge was suddenly thronged with white uniforms. It was the battalion of Guienne, arrived at the eleventh hour from its camp by the St. Charles. Some time after there was hot firing in the rear. It came from a detachment of Bougainville's command attacking a house where some of the light infantry were posted. The assailants were repulsed and the firing ceased. Light showers fell at intervals, besprinkling the troops as they stood patiently waiting the event.

Montcalm had passed a troubled night. Through all the evening the cannon bellowed from the ships of Saunders, and the boats of the fleet hovered in the dusk off the Beauport shore, threatening every moment to land. Troops lined the intrenchments till day, while the general walked the field that adjoined his head-quarters till one in the morning, accompanied by the Chevalier Johnstone and Colonel Poulariez. Johnstone says that he was in great agitation, and took no rest all night. At daybreak he heard the sound of cannon above the town. It was the battery at Samos firing on the English ships. He had sent an officer to the quarters of Vaudreuil, which were much nearer Quebec, with orders to bring him word at once should anything unusual happen. But no word came, and about six o'clock he mounted and rode thither with Johnstone. As they advanced, the country behind the town opened more and more upon their sight, till at length, when opposite Vaudreuil's house, they saw across the St. Charles, some two miles away, the red ranks of British soldiers on the heights beyond.

"This is serious business," Montcalm said, and sent off Johnstone at full gallop to bring up the troops from the center and left of the camp. Those of the right were in motion already, doubtless by the governor's order. Vaudreuil came out of the house. Montcalm stopped for a few words with him, then set spurs to his horse, and rode over the bridge of the St. Charles to the scene of danger. He rode with a fixed look, uttering not a word.

The army followed in such order as it might, crossed the bridge in hot haste, passed under the rampart of Quebec, entered at the palace gate, and pressed on in headlong march along the quaint, narrow streets of the warlike town : troops of Indians in scalp locks and war paint, a savage glitter in their deep-set eyes; bands of Canadians, whose all was at stake — faith, country, and home; the colony regulars; the battalions of old France, a torrent of white uniforms and gleaming bayonets, La Sarre, Languedoc, Roussillon, Béarn — victors of Oswego, William Henry, and Ticonderoga. So they swept on, poured out upon the plain, some by the gate of St. Louis and some by that of St. John, and hurried breathless, to where the banners of Guienne still fluttered on the ridge.

Montcalm was amazed at what he saw. He had expected a detachment, and he found an army. Full in sight before him stretched the lines of Wolfe — the close ranks of the English infantry, a silent wall of red, and the wild array of the Highlanders, with their waving tartans, and bagpipes screaming defiance.

Vaudreuil had not come; but not the less was felt the evil of a divided authority and the jealousy of the rival chiefs. Montcalm waited long for the forces he had ordered to join him from the left wing of the army. He waited in vain. It is said that the governor had detained them, lest the English should attack the Beauport shore. Even if they did so, and succeeded, the French might defy them, could they but put Wolfe to rout on the Plains of Abraham. Neither did the garri-

son at Quebec come to the aid of Montcalm. He sent
to Ramesay, its commander, for twenty-five fieldpieces
which were on the palace battery. Ramesay would
give him only three, saying that he wanted them for
his own defense. There were orders and counter-
orders; misunderstanding, haste, delay, perplexity.

Montcalm and his chief officers held a council of war.
It is said that he and they alike were for immediate
attack. His enemies declare that he was afraid lest
Vaudreuil should arrive and take command; but the
governor was not a man to assume responsibility at
such a crisis. Others say that his impetuosity over-
came his better judgment, and of this charge it is hard
to acquit him. Bougainville was but a few miles distant, and some of his troops were much nearer; a messenger sent by way of Old Lorette could have reached
him in an hour and a half at most, and a combined
attack in front and rear might have been concerted
with him. If, moreover, Montcalm could have come
to an understanding with Vaudreuil, his own force
might have been strengthened by two or three thousand additional men from the town and camp of Beauport; but he felt that there was no time to lose, for
he imagined that Wolfe would soon be reinforced,
which was impossible, and he believed that the English were fortifying themselves, which was no less an
error. He has been blamed not only for fighting too
soon, but for fighting at all. In this he could not
choose. Fight he must, for Wolfe was now in a position to cut off all his supplies. His men were full of

ardor, and he resolved to attack before their ardor cooled. He spoke a few words to them in his keen, vehement way. "I remember very well how he looked," one of the Canadians, then a boy of eighteen, used to say in his old age; "he rode a black or dark bay horse along the front of our lines, brandishing his sword, as if to excite us to do our duty. He wore a coat with wide sleeves, which fell back as he raised his arm, and showed the white linen of the wristband."

The English waited the result with a composure which, if not quite real, was at least well feigned. The three fieldpieces sent by Ramesay plied them with canister shot, and fifteen hundred Canadians and Indians fusiladed them in front and flank. Over all the plain, from behind bushes and knolls and the edge of cornfields, puffs of smoke sprang incessantly from the guns of these hidden marksmen. Skirmishers were thrown out before the lines to hold them in check, and the soldiers were ordered to lie on the grass to avoid the shot. The firing was liveliest on the English left, where bands of sharpshooters got under the edge of the declivity, among thickets, and behind scattered houses, whence they killed and wounded a considerable number of Townshend's men. The light infantry were called up from the rear. The houses were taken and retaken, and one or more of them was burned.

Wolfe was everywhere. How cool he was, and why his followers loved him, is shown by an incident that happened in the course of the morning. One of his captains was shot through the lungs, and on recovering consciousness he saw the general standing at his side. Wolfe pressed his hand, told him not to despair, praised his services, promised him early promotion, and sent an aid-de-camp to Monckton to beg that officer to keep the promise if he himself should fall.

It was toward ten o'clock when, from the high ground on the right of the line, Wolfe saw that the crisis was near. The French on the ridge had formed themselves into three bodies, regulars in the center, regulars and Canadians on right and left. Two field-pieces, which had been dragged up the heights, fired on them with grapeshot, and the troops, rising from the ground, prepared to receive them. In a few moments more they were in motion. They came on rapidly, uttering loud shouts, and firing as soon as they were within range. Their ranks, ill ordered at the best, were further confused by a number of Canadians who had been mixed among the regulars, and who, after hastily firing, threw themselves on the ground to reload. The British advanced a few rods; then halted and stood still. When the French were within forty paces the word of command rang out, and a crash of musketry answered all along the line. The volley was delivered with remarkable decision. In the battallions of the center, which had suffered least from the enemy's bullets, the simultaneous explosion was afterwards said by French officers to have sounded like cannon shot. Another volley followed, and then a furious clattering fire that lasted but a minute or two.

When the smoke rose, a miserable sight was revealed:

the ground cumbered with dead and wounded, the advancing masses stopped short and turned into a frantic mob, shouting, cursing, gesticulating. The order was given to charge. Then over the field rose the British cheer, mixed with the fierce yell of the Highland slogan. Some of the corps pushed forward with the bayonet; some advanced firing. The clansmen drew their broadswords and dashed on, keen and swift as bloodhounds. At the English right, though the attacking column was broken to pieces, a fire was still kept up, chiefly, it seems, by sharpshooters from the bushes and cornfields, where they had lain for an hour or more. Here Wolfe himself led the charge, at the head of the Louisbourg grenadiers. A shot shattered his wrist. He wrapped his handkerchief about it and kept on. Another shot struck him, and he still advanced, when a third lodged in his breast. He staggered, and sat on the ground. Lieutenant Brown of the grenadiers, one Henderson, a volunteer in the same company, and a private soldier, aided by an officer of artillery who ran to join them, carried him in their arms to the rear. He begged them to lay him down.

They did so, and asked if he would have a surgeon. "There's no need," he answered; "it's all over with me." A moment after, one of them cried out, "They run; see how they run!" "Who run?" Wolfe demanded, like a man roused from sleep. "The enemy, sir. They give way everywhere." "Go, one of you, to Colonel Burton," returned the dying man; "tell him to march Webb's regiment down to Charles River,

44

ing on
I will
soul ha
Mon
tide of
the wa
his sea
and led
open sp
eral wo
result
the stre
Dieu!
the Mai
replied
me, my

M
R

B
O

Si
T

46 FIFTH READER

And listened, while a pleased surprise
Looked from her long-lashed hazel eyes.

At last, like one who for delay
Seeks a vain excuse, he rode away.

Maud Muller looked and sighed : " Ah, me !
That I the Judge's bride might be !

" He would dress me up in silks so fine,
And praise and toast me at his wine.

" My father should wear a broadcloth coat ;
My brother should sail a painted boat.

" I'd dress my mother so grand and gay,
And the baby should have a new toy each day.

" And I'd feed the hungry and clothe the poor,
And all should bless me who left our door."

The Judge looked back as he climbed the hill,
And saw Maud Muller standing still.

" A form more fair, a face more sweet,
Ne'er hath it been my lot to meet.

" And her modest answer and graceful air
Show her wise and good as she is fair.

" Would she were mine, and I to-day,
Like her, a harvester of hay :

" No doubtful balance of rights and wrongs,
Nor weary lawyers with endless tongues,

" But low of cattle and song of birds,
And health and quiet and loving words."

But he thought of his sisters proud and cold,
And his mother vain of her rank and gold.

So, closing his heart, the Judge rode on,
And Maud was left in the field alone.

But the lawyers smiled that afternoon,
When he hummed in court an old love tune ;

And the young girl mused beside the well,
Till the rain on the unraked clover fell.

He wedded a wife of richest dower,
Who lived for fashion, as he for power.

Yet oft, in his marble hearth's bright glow,
He watched a picture come and go ;

And sweet Maud Muller's hazel eyes
Looked out in their innocent surprise.

Oft, when the wine in his glass was red,
He longed for the wayside well instead ;

And closed his eyes on his garnished rooms,
To dream of meadows and clover blooms.

And the proud man sighed, with a secret pain :
" Ah, that I were free again !

" Free as when I rode that day,
Where the barefoot maiden raked her hay."

"This basket," says he, "cost me at the wholesale merchant's a hundred drachmas, which is all I have in the world. I shall quickly make two hundred of it, by selling it in retail.

"These two hundred drachmas will in a very little while rise to four hundred, which, of course, will amount in time to four thousand. Four thousand drachmas cannot fail of making eight thousand. As soon as by these means I am master of ten thousand, I will lay aside my trade of a glassman, and turn jeweler. I shall then deal in diamonds, pearls, and all sorts of rich stones.

"When I have got together as much wealth as I well can desire, I will make a purchase of the finest house I can find, with lands, slaves, and horses. I shall then begin to enjoy myself and make a noise in the world. I will not, however, stop here, but still continue my traffic, until I have got together a hundred thousand drachmas.

"When I have thus made myself master of a hundred thousand drachmas, I shall naturally set myself on the footing of a prince, and will demand the grand vizier's daughter in marriage, after having represented to that minister the information which I have received of the beauty, wit, discretion, and other high qualities which his daughter possesses. I will let him know at the same time, that it is my intention to make him a present of a thousand pieces of gold on our marriage night.

"As soon as I have married the grand vizier's

daughter, I will buy her ten black slaves, the youngest and the best that can be got for money. I must afterward make my father-in-law a visit, with a great train and equipage. And when I am placed at his right hand, which he will do, of course, if it be only to honor his daughter, I will give him the thousand pieces of gold which I promised him; and afterward, to his great surprise, will present him with another purse of the same value, with some short speech, as, 'Sir, you see I am a man of my word; I always give more than I promise.'

"When I have brought the princess to my house, I shall take particular care to train her to a due respect for me. To this end I shall confine her to her own apartment, make her a short visit, and talk but little to her. Her women will represent to me that she is inconsolable by reason of my unkindness, and beg me with tears to love her, and let her sit down by me; but I shall still remain inexorable.

"Her mother will then come and bring her daughter to me, as I am seated upon my sofa. The daughter, with tears in her eyes, will fling herself at my feet, and beg of me to receive her into my favor. Then will I, to imprint in her a thorough veneration for my person, draw up my legs and spurn her from me with my foot, in such a manner that she shall fall down several paces from the sofa."

Alnaschar was entirely swallowed up in this chimerical vision, and could not forbear acting with his foot what he had in his thoughts; so that unluckily striking his basket of brittle ware, which was the foundation of all his grandeur, he kicked his glasses to a great distance from him into the street, and broke them into ten thousand pieces.

———◆———

THE BLUE AND THE GRAY

FRANCIS MILES FINCH

By the flow of the inland river,
　　Whence the fleets of iron have fled,
Where the blades of the grave grass quiver,
　　Asleep are the ranks of the dead : —
　　　Under the sod and the dew,
　　　　Waiting the judgment day ;
　　　Under the one, the Blue ;
　　　　Under the other, the Gray.

Those, in the robings of glory,
　　These, in the gloom of defeat.
All with the battle blood gory,
　　In the dusk of eternity meet ; —
　　　Under the sod and the dew,
　　　　Waiting the judgment day ; —
　　　Under the laurel, the Blue ;
　　　　Under the willow, the Gray.

From the silence of sorrowful hours
　　The desolate mourners go,
Lovingly laden with flowers
　　Alike for the friend and the foe ; —

Under the sod and the dew,
　　Waiting the judgment day ; —
Under the roses, the Blue ;
　　Under the lilies, the Gray.

So with an equal splendor
　The morning sun rays fall,
With a touch, impartially tender,
　On the blossoms blooming for all ; —
　　Under the sod and the dew,
　　　Waiting the judgment day ; —
　　'Broidered with gold, the Blue ;
　　　Mellowed with gold, the Gray.

So, when the summer calleth,
　On forest and field of grain,
With an equal murmur falleth
　The cooling drip of the rain ; —
　　Under the sod and the dew,
　　　Waiting the judgment day ; —
　　Wet with the rain, the Blue ;
　　　Wet with the rain, the Gray.

Sadly, but not with upbraiding,
　The generous deed was done ;
In the storm of the years that are fading,
　No braver battle was won ; —
　　Under the sod and the dew,
　　　Waiting the judgment day ;
　　Under the blossoms, the Blue ;
　　　Under the garlands, the Gray.

No more shall the war cry sever,
  Or the winding rivers be red;
They banish our anger forever
   When they laurel the graves of our dead; —
    Under the sod and the dew,
     Waiting the judgment day; —
    Love and tears for the Blue;
    Tears and love for the Gray.

THE DESTRUCTION OF SENNACHERIB

Lord Byron

The Assyrian came down like the wolf on the fold,
And his cohorts were gleaming in purple and gold;
And the sheen of their spears was like stars on the sea,
When the blue wave rolls nightly on deep Galilee.

Like the leaves of the forest when summer is green,
That host with their banners at sunset were seen:
Like the leaves of the forest when autumn hath blown,
That host on the morrow lay withered and strown.

For the Angel of Death spread his wings on the blast,
And breathed in the face of the foe as he passed;
And the eyes of the sleepers waxed deadly and chill,
And their hearts but once heaved, and forever grew still!

And there lay the steed with his nostril all wide,
But through it there rolled not the breath of his pride;

And the foam of his gasping lay white on the turf,
And cold as the spray of the rock-beating surf.

And there lay the rider distorted and pale,
With the dew on his brow and the rust on his mail:
And the tents were all silent, the banners alone,
The lances unlifted, the trumpet unblown.

And the widows of Asshur are loud in their wail,
And the idols are broke in the temple of Baal;
And the might of the Gentile, unsmote by the sword,
Hath melted like snow in the glance of the Lord !

A RUFFIAN IN FEATHERS

OLIVE THORNE MILLER

WE all know Shakespeare's opinion of the "man that hath no music in himself," although we usually misquote it. If this be a fair judgment of the human race, how much more justly may it be said of the bird, to whom we look for the sweetest harmonies of nature!

I do not think his best friend will claim that the common house sparrow has the soul of music in him; certainly not if he has ever been wakened in a glorious dawn by the indescribable jangle of harsh sounds which constitute this bird's only morning hymn, at the hour when every bird in the woods, from the noble singers of the thrush family down to the least chipping sparrow, is greeting the new day in his most musical fashion.

The matin song of the house sparrow, in which he indulges unsparingly, being of similar quality, harmonizes perfectly with the jarring sounds of man's contriving: the clatter of iron-shod wheels over city pavements, the war whoop of the ferocious milkman, the unearthly cries of the venders, and above all the junkman's pandemonium of "bells jangled out of tune." The harshest cries of our native birds, if not always musical in themselves, seem at least to accord in some way with sounds of nature. The house sparrow alone is entirely discordant — the one bird without a pleasing note, whose very love song is an unmusical squeak. Nor is his appearance more interesting than his voice, and on looking into his manners and customs we discover most unlovely characteristics.

One of the most familiar habits of this graceless bird is his delight in a mob. No sooner does anything occur to disturb the even tenor of sparrow life, whether a domestic skirmish, the first outing of a young family, or some danger to a nest, than a crowd collects, not only as interested spectators, but quite ready and willing to take a hand in any sport or crime that is going; not only a hand, but a voice as well. Loud cries always announce when a rabble is at work. Whether, as is declared by some observers, they drive away our native birds by this means I am not sure. I have seen them annoy the catbird, the robin, and the Baltimore oriole, but in each case they were put to flight by the native bird; though no doubt the experience is sufficiently disagreeable to induce any one of these birds to

select a more retired neighborhood for nest building.
I once noticed the same tactics successfully applied to
a cat which climbed up among the nests.

An amusing instance in which the birds were worsted
took place under my eye last summer. Hearing the
usual outcry one morning, I looked out, and saw a
great crowd of sparrows perched on the branches of a
tall maple tree, shrieking at the top of their voices,
craning their necks, and hopping ever nearer to one of
the houses so kindly provided for their use. It was
not one of the four-story hotel arrangements with
which we disfigure our trees, but a single cottage, with
room for but one couple, and it was quite high up in
the tree. The excitement centered around this house,
and for a long time I could not see what was the dis-
turbing cause. Close watching with a glass at length
revealed a small reddish head, with very sharp eyes,
occupying the doorway of the cottage, and after some
time the owner of these features calmly stepped out on
the veranda and showed himself — a small red squirrel,
with a silver collar, which proclaimed him an escaped
pet. He looked thin, with a tail almost as bare as a
rat's. He had evidently not fared well in captivity,
and I rejoiced in his freedom.

But the sparrow world had decided to eject him from
the neighborhood, and faithfully, with true sparrow
doggedness, they worked at this problem. No sooner
did he appear than they resumed their attack, flying
around him, screaming, and making quick dashes at
him. He was somewhat disconcerted, and ran up a

long branch, followed by the whole gang, which grew
more bold as he apparently retreated, dashing ever
nearer as though to peck him, but never actually touching him.   While he was running they were very bold,
but the moment he sat up and faced them they drew
off a little, though they never went quite away.   For
several days not a movement of his escaped their notice.
It was amusing to see how quickly the smallest stir on
his part was announced to the world.   " There he is !
He's coming out ! " one could easily understand, and
every sparrow within hearing responded by instantly
deserting his business or pleasure, and adding his presence and cries to the mob.

But the squirrel, finding fruit trees with green apples
and pears, resolved to stay, and after a week or two
they became so far accustomed to his presence as to be
less alarmed, though they never lost interest in him.
His eating especially seemed to divert and astonish
them.   I have seen fifty birds at once hovering around
an evergreen tree, too small to afford them perching
places, far enough from the enemy, while he gathered
and nibbled the small cones.   When he sat up on a
branch, holding a green pear in his tiny paws, their
amusement knew no bounds.   They sat around at a
safe distance, exchanging remarks in the amiable manner of some of the human race at the ways of a for-
eigner.

The squirrel had by this time resumed his wild in-
stincts, cared nothing for them, and would even answer
back with a sharp little cry.   He had taken up his sum-

mer residence in the maple-tree cottage, and all through the fall, while pears hung on the trees of the neglected yard next ours, he lived in clover. His tail became bushy, his coat grew sleek, and he looked like a different animal. Still the sparrows attended his every movement, following him like a train of courtiers wherever he went, though they did not make quite so much noise about it as at first.

The household became as keenly interested as the birds in the doings of the pretty fellow. All through the winter he appeared on the mild days, running and bounding all over the tall maples. We saw him gather grass and carry it off in great bundles in his mouth to make a bed, and after an unusually cold season he spent part of two days in removing his residence from an ornamental pile of stones in a neighbor's yard to some place he had discovered under the house. He had evidently collected a quantity of stores of some sort. No doubt as soon as spring opened he would vary his diet with fresh eggs, but as I left the vicinity I did not have opportunity to observe whether the sparrow family suffered from him, though I noticed that he had changed his dwelling to a hole in the maple above mentioned.

Next to the sparrow's mobbing propensity is his impudence. Not only will he insist on sharing the food of chickens and domestic animals, but he is a common guest at the table of the great bald eagles in the parks, and does not disdain the crumbs that fall from the repast of the polar bear, one touch of whose paw would flatten him like a wafer.

Perhaps the most saucy thing reported of a sparrow was witnessed in Brooklyn by a well-known artist. He was watching a robin hard at work on the lawn, gathering food for his family, when he noticed a sparrow who also seemed interested in the operation. The sparrow looked on, evidently with growing excitement, while one bit after another was uncovered, till at last a particularly large and attractive grub was brought to light. This was too much for sparrow philosophy. He made one dash, snatched the tempting morsel from the very bill of the robin, and disappeared before the astounded bird recovered from his surprise.

With this unparalleled act of impertinence to a bird big enough to eat him, this true chronicle of the most unattractive fellow that wears feathers shall close.

THE RISING IN 1776

THOMAS BUCHANAN READ

OUT of the North the wild news came,
Far flashing on its wings of flame,
Swift as the boreal light which flies
At midnight through the startled skies.

And there was tumult in the air,
    The fife's shrill note, the drum's loud beat,
And through the wide land everywhere
    The answering tread of hurrying feet;

While the first oath of Freedom's gun
Came on the blast from Lexington;
And Concord roused, no longer tame,
Forgot her old baptismal name,
Made bare her patriot's arm of power,
And swelled the discord of the hour.

. . . .

Within its shade of elm and oak
    The church of Berkeley Manor stood;
There Sunday found the rural folk,
    And some esteemed of gentle blood.
In vain their feet, with loitering tread,
    Passed 'mid the graves where rank is naught;
    All could not read the lesson taught
In that republic of the dead.

How sweet the hour of Sabbath talk,
    The vale with peace and sunshine full,
Where all the happy people walk,
    Decked in their homespun flax and wool!
Where youths' gay hats with blossoms bloom,
    And every maid, with simple art,
    Wears on her breast, like her own heart,
A bud whose depths are all perfume;
While every garment's gentle stir
Is breathing rose and lavender.

. . . .

The pastor came: his snowy locks
    Hallowed his brow of thought and care;
And calmly, as shepherds lead their flocks,
    He led into the house of prayer.

Then soon he rose ;　the prayer was strong ;
The psalm was warrior David's song ;
The text, a few short words of might ;
" The Lord of hosts shall arm the right ! "

He spoke of wrongs too long endured,
Of sacred rights to be secured ;
Then from his patriot tongue of flame
The startling words for Freedom came.
The stirring sentences he spake
Compelled the heart to glow or quake,
And, rising on his theme's broad wing,
　　And grasping in his nervous hand
　　The imaginary battle brand,
In face of death he dared to fling
Defiance to a tyrant king.

Even as he spoke, his frame, renewed
In eloquence of attitude,
Rose, as it seemed, a shoulder higher ;
Then swept his kindling glance of fire
From startled pew to breathless choir ;
When suddenly his mantle wide
His hands impatient flung aside,
And, lo ! he met their wondering eyes
Complete in all a warrior's guise.

A moment there was awful pause —
When Berkeley cried, " Cease, traitor ! cease ;
God's temple is the house of peace ! "
　　The other shouted, " Nay ! not so,
　　When God is with our righteous cause ;

THE SPIRIT OF '76.

His holiest places then are ours,
His temples are our forts and towers
   That frown upon the tyrant foe ;
In this, the dawn of Freedom's day,
There is a time to fight and pray ! "

And now before the open door —
   The warrior priest had ordered so —
The enlisting trumpet's sudden roar
Rang through the chapel, o'er and o'er,
   Its long reverberating blow,
So loud and clear, it seemed the ear
Of dusty death must wake and hear.
And there the startling drum and fife
Fired the living with fiercer life ;
While overhead, with wild increase,
Forgetting its ancient toll of peace,
   The great bell swung as ne'er before.
It seemed as it would never cease ;
And every word its ardor flung
From off its jubilant iron tongue
   Was " War ! War ! War ! "

" Who dares " — this was the patriot's cry,
   As striding from the desk he came, —
   " Come out with me, in Freedom's name,
For her to live, for her to die ? "
A hundred hands flung up reply,
A hundred voices answered, " I ! "

ESKIMO DOG TEAMS

ELISHA KENT KANE

EVERY schoolboy knows that the hardy Eskimos, warmly clad in furs, take long journeys, during the Arctic winters, on sledges, drawn by dog teams. Dr. Kane gives the following account of a meeting with a party of Eskimos:

"I went up from the cabin, followed by as many as could mount the gangway; and there they were, on all sides of the rocky harbor, dotting the snow shores and emerging from the blackness of the cliffs, — wild and uncouth, but evidently human beings.

"Their leader, like a brave fellow, leaped down the floe, and advanced to meet me halfway. He was nearly a head taller than myself, extremely powerful and well built, with swarthy complexion and piercing black eyes. His dress was a hooded *capôte*, or jumper, of mixed white and blue fox-pelts, arranged with something of fancy, and booted trousers of white bearskin, which, at the end of the foot, were made to terminate with the claws of the animals.

"Although this was the first time he had ever seen a white man, he went with me fearlessly into the cabin, his companions remaining behind on the ice.

"I soon sent word to the others, and they brought up from behind the land ice as many as fifty-six fine dogs, with their sledges, and secured them within two hundred feet of the brig, driving their lances into the ice, and picketing the dogs to them by the seal-skin traces. When they were first allowed to come on board, they were very rude and difficult to manage. They were incessantly in motion, going everywhere, trying doors, and squeezing themselves through dark passages, round casks and boxes, and out into the light again, anxious to touch and handle everything they saw, and asking for, or else endeavoring to steal, everything they touched. . . .

" They ate their walrus meat on the ice. They did not eat all at once, but each man, when and as often, as impulse prompted him. Each slept after eating, his raw chunk lying beside him ; and, as he woke, the first act was to eat, and the next to sleep again. They did not lie down, but slumbered away in a sitting posture, with the head declined upon the breast, some of them snoring famously.

" In the morning they were anxious to go. I gave them leave ; they yoked in their dogs in less than two minutes, got on their sledges, cracked their fifteen feet long seal-skin whips, and were off down the ice to the southwest at a rate of seven knots an hour.

" The Eskimo dog is driven by a single trace, a long thin thong of seal or walrus hide, which passes from his chest over his haunches to the sledge. The team is always driven abreast, and the traces are, of course, tangling and twisting themselves up incessantly, as the half-wild or terrified brutes bound right or left from their prescribed positions.

" The consequence is, that the seven, or nine, or

fourteen lines have a marvelous aptitude at knotting themselves up beyond the reach of skill and patience. If the weather is warm enough to thaw the snow, the lines become soft, and the knots may be untied ; but

in cold weather, the knife must be used to cut the traces.

"The dog whip is six yards long, and the handle but sixteen inches, — rather a short lever, to throw out such a length of seal hide. Learn to do it, however, with a masterly sweep, or else make up your mind to forego driving sledge ; for the dogs are guided solely by the lash, and you must be able, not only to hit any particular dog out of the team of twelve, but also to accompany the feat with a resounding crack. After this, you find that to get your lash back involves another difficulty ; for it is apt to entangle itself among the dogs and lines, or to fasten itself cunningly round bits of ice, so as to drag you head over heels into the snow.

" The secret by which this complicated set of requirements is fulfilled consists in properly describing an arc from the shoulder, with a stiff elbow, giving the jerk to the whip handle from the hand and wrist alone. The lash trails behind you as you travel, and, when thrown forward, is allowed to extend itself without an effort to bring it back.

" You wait patiently after giving the projected impulse until it unwinds its slow length, reaches the end of its tether, and cracks to tell you that it is at its journey's end. Such a crack on the ear or forefoot of an unfortunate dog is signalized by a howl quite unmistakable in its import.

" The mere labor of using this whip is such that the Eskimos travel in couples, one sledge after the other. The hinder dogs follow mechanically, and thus require no whip ; and the drivers change about so as to rest each other."

$$\longrightarrow\!\!\blacklozenge\!\!\longleftarrow$$

AN ORDER FOR A PICTURE

Alice Cary

Oh, good painter, tell me true,
    Has your hand the cunning to draw
    Shapes of things that you never saw ?
Ay ? Well, here is an order for you.

Woods and cornfields a little brown, —
    The picture must not be over bright, —
    Yet all in the golden and gracious light
Of a cloud when the summer sun is down.

Alway and alway, night and morn,
Woods upon woods, with fields of corn
    Lying between them, not quite sere
And not in the full, thick, leafy bloom,
When the wind can hardly find breathing room
    Under their tassels, — cattle near,
Biting shorter the short green grass,
And a hedge of sumac and sassafras,
With bluebirds twittering all around, —
Ah, good painter, you can't paint sound !

These and the little house where I was born,
    Low and little and black and old,
    With children, many as it can hold,
All at the windows, open wide, —
Heads and shoulders clear outside,
And fair young faces all ablush ;
    Perhaps you may have seen, some day,
    Roses crowding the self-same way,
Out of a wilding, wayside bush.

Listen closer.   When you have done
    With woods and cornfields and grazing herds,
A lady, the loveliest ever the sun
Looked down upon, you must paint for me ;

Oh, if I only could make you see
    The clear blue eyes, the tender smile,
The sovereign sweetness, the gentle grace,
The woman's soul and the angel's face
    That are beaming on me all the while!
I need not speak these foolish words;
Yet one word tells you all I would say, —
    She is my mother; you will agree
That all the rest may be thrown away.

    Two little urchins at her knee
    You must paint, sir, one like me, —
The other with a clearer brow,
And the light of his adventurous eyes
Flashing with boldest enterprise:
    At ten years old he went to sea, —
God knoweth if he be living now, —
He sailed in the good ship *Commodore*, —
    Nobody ever crossed her track
    To bring us news, and she never came back.

Ah, 'tis twenty long years and more,
Since that old ship went out of the bay
    With my great-hearted brother on her deck:
    I watched him till he shrank to a speck,
And his face was toward me all the way.
Bright his hair was, a golden brown,
    The time we stood at our mother's knee;
That beauteous head, if it did go down,
    Carried sunshine into the sea!

Out in the field one summer night
  We were together, half afraid
  Of the corn-leaves' rustling, and of the shade
Of the high hills, stretching so still and far, —
Loitering till after the low little light
Of the candle shone through the open door,
  And, over the haystack's pointed top,
  All of a tremble, and ready to drop,
    The first half-hour, the great yellow star,
  That we, with staring, ignorant eyes,
Had often and often watched to see
  Propped and held in its place in the skies
By the fork of a tall red mulberry tree,
Which close in the edge of our flax field grew, —
  Dead at the top, — just one branch full
  Of leaves, notched round, and lined with wool,
From which it tenderly shook the dew
  Over our heads when we came to play
  In its handbreadth of shadow day after day.

Afraid to go home, sir ; for one of us bore
A nest full of speckled and thin-shelled eggs, —
The other, a bird, held fast by the legs,
Not so big as a straw of wheat :
The berries we gave her she wouldn't eat,
But cried and cried, till we held her bill,
So slim and shining, to keep her still.

At last we stood at our mother's knee.
    Do you think, sir, if you try,
    You can paint the look of a lie ?

If you can, pray have the grace
    To put it solely in the face
Of the urchin that is likest me ;
    I think 'twas solely mine, indeed :
But that's no matter, — paint it so.
    The eyes of our mother — take good heed —
    Looking not on the nest full of eggs,
Nor the fluttering bird held so fast by the legs,
But straight through our faces down to our lies,
And oh, with such injured, reproachful surprise,
I felt my heart bleed where that glance went, as though
    A sharp blade struck through it.

        You, sir, know,
That you on the canvas are to repeat
Things that are fairest, things most sweet, —
Woods and cornfields and mulberry tree, —
The mother, — the lads, with their bird, at her knee ;
    But, oh, that look of reproachful woe !
High as the heavens your name I'll shout,
If you paint me the picture, and leave that out.

                    — *By permission of Houghton, Mifflin & Co.*

*If you wish to be miserable, you must think about your-
self ; about what you want, what you like, what respect
people ought to pay you, what people think of you ; and
then to you nothing will be pure.   You will spoil everything you touch ; you will make sin and misery out of
everything God sends you ; you can be as wretched as you
choose.*
                                    — Kingsley.

THE LAND OF SOULS

AN INDIAN LEGEND

HENRY R. SCHOOLCRAFT

THERE was once a beautiful girl, who died suddenly on the day she was to have been married to a handsome young hunter. He had also proved his bravery in war, so that he enjoyed the praises of his tribe; but his heart was not proof against this loss. From the hour she was buried, there was no more joy or peace for him. He went often to visit the spot where the women had buried her, and sat musing there, when, it was thought by some of his friends, he would have done better to try to amuse himself in the chase, or by diverting his thoughts in the warpath. But war and hunting had lost their charms for him. His heart was already dead within him. He wholly neglected both his war club and his bow and arrows.

He had heard the old people say that there was a path that led to the land of souls, and he determined to follow it. He accordingly set out, one morning, after having completed his preparations for the journey. At first he hardly knew which way to go. He was only guided by the tradition that he must go south. For a while he could see no change in the face of the country. Forests and hills, and valleys and streams, had the same looks which they wore in his native place. There was snow on the ground when he set out, and it was sometimes seen to be piled and matted on the thick trees and bushes. At length it began to diminish, and, as he walked on, finally disappeared. The forest assumed a more cheerful appearance, the leaves put forth their buds, and before he was aware of the completeness of the change, he found he had left behind him the land of snow and ice. The air became pure and mild, the dark clouds had rolled away from the sky, a pure field of blue was above him, and, as he went forward in his journey, he saw flowers beside his path, and heard the song of birds. By these signs he knew that he was going the right way, for they agreed with the traditions of his tribe.

At length he spied a path. It took him through a grove, then up a long and elevated ridge, on the very top of which he came to a lodge. At the door stood an old man, with white hair, whose eyes though deeply sunk, had a fiery brilliancy. He had a long robe of skins thrown loosely around his shoulders, and a staff in his hands.

The young man began to tell his story, but the venerable chief arrested him before he had proceeded to speak ten words. "I have expected you," he replied, "and had just risen to bid you welcome to my abode. She whom you seek passed here but a short time since, and, being fatigued with her journey, rested herself here. Enter my lodge and be seated, and I will then satisfy your inquiries and give you directions for your journey from this point." Having done this, and refreshed himself by rest, they both issued forth from the lodge door. "You see yonder gulf," said the chief, "and the wide-stretching plain beyond. It is the land of souls. You stand upon its borders, and my lodge is the gate of entrance. But you cannot take your body along. Leave it here with your bow and arrows, your bundle, and your dog. You will find them safe upon your return."

So saying, he reëntered the lodge, and the freed traveler bounded forward, as if his feet had suddenly been endowed with the power of wings. But all things retained their natural colors and shapes. The woods and leaves, and streams and lakes, were only more bright and comely than he had ever witnessed. Animals bounded across his path with a freedom and a confidence which seemed to tell him there was no bloodshed there. Birds of beautiful plumage inhabited the groves and sported in the waters. There was but one thing in which he saw a very unusual effect. He noticed that his passage was not stopped by trees or other objects. He appeared to walk directly through them. They were, in fact, but the images or shadows of material trees. He became sensible that he was in the land of souls.

When he had traveled half a day's journey, through a country which was continually becoming more attractive, he came to the banks of a broad lake, in the center of which was a large and beautiful island. He found a canoe of white shining stone tied to the shore. He was now sure that he had come the right path, for the aged man had told him of this. There were also shining paddles. He immediately entered the canoe, and took the paddles in his hand, when, to his joy and surprise, on turning round he beheld the object of his search in another canoe exactly its counterpart in everything. It seemed to be the shadow of his own. She had exactly imitated his motions, and they were side by side.

They at once pushed out from the shore, and began to cross the lake. Its waves seemed to be rising, and, at a distance, looked ready to swallow them up ; but just as they entered the whitened edge of them they seemed to melt away, as if they were but the images of waves. But no sooner was one wreath of foam passed than another, more threatening still, rose up. Thus they were in perpetual fear ; but what added to it was the clearness of the water, through which they could see heaps of bones of beings who had perished before.

The Master of Life had, however, decreed to let them pass, for the thoughts and acts of neither of them had been bad. But they saw many others struggling and sinking in the waves. Old men and young men, males and females, of all ages and ranks, were there : some passed and some sank. It was only the little children whose canoes seemed to meet no waves.

At length every difficulty was gone, as in a moment, and they both leaped out on the happy island. They felt that the very air was food. It strengthened and nourished them. They wandered together over the blissful fields, where everything was formed to please the eye and the ear. There were no tempests; there was no ice, nor chilly winds; no one shivered for the want of warm clothes; no one suffered for hunger; no one mourned for the dead. They saw no graves. They heard of no wars. Animals ran freely about, but there was no blood spilled in hunting them; for the air itself nourished them.

Gladly would the young warrior have remained there forever, but he was obliged to go back for his body. He did not see the Master of Life, but he heard his voice, as if it were a soft breeze.

"Go back," said the voice, "to the land from whence you came. Your time has not yet come. The duties for which I made you, and which you are to perform, are not yet finished. Return to your people, and accomplish the acts of a good man. You, will be the ruler of your tribe for many days. The rules you will observe will be told you by my messenger, who keeps the gate. When he surrenders back your body, he will tell you what to do. Listen to him, and you shall afterward rejoin the spirit which you have followed, but whom you must now leave behind. She is accepted, and will be ever here, as young and as happy as she was when I first called her from the land of snows."

When this voice ceased the warrior awoke. It was the fancy work of a dream, and he was still in the bitter land of snows and hunger, death and tears.

GRADATIM

Josiah Gilbert Holland

HEAVEN is not reached by a single bound,
   But we build the ladder by which we rise
   From the lowly earth to the vaulted skies,
And we mount to its summit round by round.

I count this thing to be grandly true,
   That a noble deed is a step toward God,
   Lifting the soul from the common clod
To a purer air and a fairer view.

We rise by the things that are under our feet,
   By what we have mastered of good or gain;
   By the pride deposed, or the passion slain,
And the vanquished ills that we hourly meet.

We hope, we aspire, we resolve, we trust,
   When the morning calls to life and light;
   But our hearts grow weary, and ere the night
Our lives are trailing the sordid dust.

We hope, we resolve, we aspire, we pray;
   And we think that we mount the air on wings
   Beyond the recall of earthly things,
While our feet still cling to the heavy clay.

Wings are for angels, but feet for men!
   We may borrow the wings to find the way;

We may hope, and resolve, and aspire, and pray,
But our feet must rise or we fall again.

Only in dreams is a ladder thrown
    From the weary earth to the sapphire walls;
    But the dreams depart and the ladder falls,
And the sleeper wakes on his pillow of stone.

Heaven is not reached at a single bound,
    But we build the ladder by which we rise
    From the lowly earth to the vaulted skies,
And we mount to its summit round by round.

UNDER THE GREENWOOD TREE

WILLIAM SHAKESPEARE

UNDER the greenwood tree
Who loves to lie with me,
And tune his merry note
Unto the sweet bird's throat,
Come hither, come hither, come hither:
    Here shall we see
    No enemy
But winter and rough weather.

Who doth ambition shun,
And loves to live in the sun,
Seeking the food he eats,
And pleased with what he gets,

would otherwise be too slack, it is stretched tight and
fixed to the wall in the same manner as before.

In this way it spins and fixes several threads parallel
to one another, which, so to speak, serve as the warp to
the intended web. To form the woof, it spins in the
same manner its thread, transversely fixing one end to
the first thread that was spun, and which is always the
strongest of the whole web, and the other to the wall.
All these threads, being newly spun, are glutinous, and
therefore stick to one another whenever they happen to
touch ; and in those parts of the web most likely to be
torn, our natural artist strengthens them by doubling
the thread sometimes sixfold.

I perceived, about four years ago, a large spider, in
one corner of my room, making its web ; and, though
the servant leveled her fatal broom against the labors
of the little animal, I had the good fortune then to prevent its destruction.

In three days, the web was completed ; nor could I
avoid thinking that the insect seemed to exult in living
in its new abode.   It repeatedly traversed it round, and
examined the strength of every part of it, retired into its
hole, and came out very frequently.   The first enemy,
however, it had to encounter, was another and a much
larger spider, which, having no web of its own, and having probably exhausted all of its stock in former labors of
this kind, came to invade the property of its neighbor.
Soon, then, a terrible encounter followed, in which
the invader seemed to have the victory, and the laborious spider was obliged to take refuge in its hole.

Upon this I perceived the victor using every art to draw the enemy from its stronghold. He seemed to go off, but quickly returned, and when he found all his arts vain he began to destroy the new web without mercy. This brought on another battle, and, contrary to my expectations, the laborious spider became conqueror, and fairly killed its antagonist.

Now, then, in peaceful possession of what was its own, it waited three days with the utmost patience, repairing the breaks of its web, and taking no food that I could perceive. At last, however, a large blue fly fell into the snare, and struggled hard to get loose. The spider gave it leave to entangle itself as much as possible, but it seemed to be too strong for the cobweb.

I once put a wasp into the nest, but when the spider came out to seize it as usual, upon perceiving what kind of an enemy it had to deal with, it instantly broke all the bands that held it fast, and contributed all that lay in its power to disengage so powerful an antagonist. When the wasp was at liberty, I expected that the spider would have set about repairing the breaks in the net; but this, it seems, could not be accomplished, therefore the cobweb was now entirely forsaken, and a new one begun.

I had now a mind to try how many cobwebs a single spider could furnish; therefore I destroyed this, and the insect set about another. When I destroyed the other also, its whole stock seemed entirely exhausted, and it could spin no more. The arts it made use of to support itself, now deprived of its great means of subsistence, were indeed surprising. I have seen it roll up its legs like a ball, and lie motionless for hours together, but cautiously watching all the time; when a fly happened to approach sufficiently near, it would dart out all at once, and often seize its prey.

Of this life, however, it soon began to grow weary, and resolved to invade the possession of some other spider, since it could not make a web of its own. It made an attack upon a neighboring web with great vigor, and at first was as vigorously repulsed. Not daunted, however, with one defeat, in this manner it continued to lay siege to another's web for three days, and at length having killed the defendant, actually took possession.

When smaller flies happen to fall into the snare, the spider does not sally out at once, but very patiently waits till it is sure of them; for should it immediately approach, the terror of its appearance might give the captive strength sufficient to get loose; its habit then is to wait patiently, till, by useless struggles, the captive has wasted all its strength, and then it becomes a certain and easy conquest.

The insect I am now describing lived three years; every year it changed its skin and got a new set of legs. I have sometimes plucked off a leg, which grew again in two or three days. At first it dreaded my approach to its web, but at last it became so familiar as to take a fly out of my hand, and upon my touching any part of the web, would immediately leave its hole, prepared either for defense or an attack.

To complete this description it may be observed that the male spiders are much smaller than the female. When the latter come to lay, they spread a part of their web under the eggs, and then roll them up carefully, as we roll up things in a cloth, and thus hatch them in their hole. If disturbed, they never attempt to escape without carrying their young brood in their forceps away with them, and thus frequently are sacrificed to their parental affection.

As soon as ever the young ones leave their artificial covering they begin to spin, and almost sensibly seem to grow bigger. If they have the good fortune, when but a day old, to catch a fly, they begin to eat with good appetites; but they live sometimes three or four days without any sustenance, and continue to grow larger very rapidly.

As they grow old, however, they do not continue to increase in size. Their legs, only, grow longer. And when a spider becomes entirely stiff with age, and unable to seize its prey, it dies at length of hunger.

PERSEVERANCE

FANCY thou not, though weary, as if won
The journey's end when only just begun;
For not a mountain peak with Toil attained
But shows a top yet higher to be gained.
Wherefore, still Forward, Forward!

TO DAFFODILS

ROBERT HERRICK

FAIR Daffodils, we weep to see
   You haste away so soon :
As yet the early-rising sun
   Has not attain'd his noon.
     Stay, stay,
   Until the hasting day
     Has run
   But to the even song ;
And, having pray'd together, we
   Will go with you along.

We have short time to stay, as you,
   We have as short a spring ;
As quick a growth to meet decay,
   As you, or anything.
     We die,
   As your hours do, and dry
     Away,
   Like to the summer's rain ;
Or as the pearls of morning's dew
   Ne'er to be found again.

Howe'er it be, it seems to me
'Tis only noble to be good.

           — *Tennyson.*

HORSESHOE ROBINSON'S RUSE

A STORY OF THE REVOLUTIONARY WAR

John P. Kennedy

On the morning that succeeded the night in which Horseshoe Robinson arrived at Musgrove's, the stout and honest sergeant might have been seen, about eight o'clock, leaving the main road from Ninety Six at the point where that leading to David Ramsay's separated from it, and cautiously urging his way into the deep forest by the more private path into which he had entered. The knowledge that Innis was encamped along the Ennoree, within a short distance of the mill, had compelled him to make an extensive circuit to reach Ramsay's dwelling, whither he was now bent ; and he had experienced considerable delay in his morning journey, by finding himself frequently in the neighborhood of small foraging parties of Tories, whose motions he was obliged to watch for fear of an encounter. He had once already been compelled to use his horse's heels in what he called "fair flight," and once to ensconce himself a full half-hour under cover of the thicket afforded him by a swamp. He now, therefore, according to his own phrase, "dived into the little road that scrambled down through the woods toward Ramsay's, with all his eyes about him, looking out as sharply as a fox on a foggy morning," and, with this circumspection, he was not long in arriving within view of Ramsay's house. Like a practiced soldier, whom frequent frays have taught wisdom, he resolved to reconnoiter before he advanced upon a post that might be in possession of an enemy. He therefore dismounted, fastened his horse in a fence corner, where a field of corn concealed him from notice, and then stealthily crept forward until he came immediately behind one of the outhouses.

The barking of a house dog brought out a negro boy, to whom Robinson instantly addressed the query, —

" Is your master at home ? "

" No, sir. He's got his horse, and gone off more than an hour ago."

" Where is your mistress ? "

" Shelling beans, sir."

" I didn't ask you," said the sergeant, " what she is doing, but where she is."

" In course, she is in the house, sir," replied the negro, with a grin.

" Any strangers there ? "

" There was plenty of 'em a little while ago, but they've been gone a good while."

Robinson, having thus satisfied himself as to the safety of his visit, directed the boy to take his horse and lead him up to the door. He then entered the dwelling.

" Mrs. Ramsay," said he, walking up to the dame, who was occupied at a table, with a large trencher before her, in which she was plying that household thrift which the negro described, " luck to you, ma'am, and all your house ! "

"Good lack, Mr. Horseshoe Robinson!" exclaimed the matron, offering the sergeant her hand. "What has brought you here? What news? Who are with you?"

"I am alone," said Robinson, as he took off his hat and shook the water from it; "it has just begun to rain, and it looks as if it was going to give us enough of it. You don't mind doing a little dinner work of a Sunday, I see: shelling of beans, I suppose, is tantamount to dragging a sheep out of a pond, as the preachers allow on the Sabbath — ha, ha! Where's Davy?"

"He's gone over to the meetinghouse on Ennoree, hoping to hear something of the army at Camden. Perhaps you can tell us the news from that quarter?"

"Faith, that's a mistake, Mrs. Ramsay. Though at this present speaking I command the flying artillery. We have but one man in the corps — and that's myself; and all the guns we have is this piece of ordnance that hangs in this old belt by my side" (pointing to his sword), "and that I captured from the enemy at Blackstock's. I was hoping I might find John Ramsay at home: I have need of him as a recruit."

"Ah, Mr. Robinson, John has a heavy life of it over there with Sumter. We thought that he might have been here to-day; yet I am glad he didn't come, for he would have been certain to get into trouble. Who should come in this morning, just after my husband had cleverly got away on his horse, but a young ensign that belongs to Ninety Six, and four great Scotchmen

with him, all in red coats ; they had been out thieving,
I warrant, and were now going home again. And who
but they ! Here they were, swaggering all about my
house, and calling for this and calling for that, as if they
owned the fee simple of everything on the plantation.
And it made my blood rise, Mr. Horseshoe, to see them
run out in the yard and catch up my chickens and ducks
and kill as many as they could string about them, and
I not daring to say a word — though I did give them a
piece of my mind, too."

"Who is at home with you?" inquired the sergeant.

"Nobody but my youngest boy, Andrew," answered
the dame. "And then the toping rioters — " she continued, exalting her voice.

"What arms have you in the house?" asked Robinson, without heeding the dame's rising anger.

"We have a rifle, and a horseman's pistol that
belongs to John. They must call for drink, too,
and turn my house, of a Sunday morning, into a
tavern — "

"They took the route toward Ninety Six, you said,
Mrs. Ramsay?"

"Yes, they went straight forward upon the road.
But, look you, Mr. Horseshoe, you're not thinking of
going after them?"

"Isn't there an old field, about a mile from this, on
that road?" inquired the sergeant, still intent upon
his own thought.

"There is," replied the dame, "with the old school-
house upon it."

"A lopsided, rickety log cabin in the middle of the field. Am I right, good woman?"

"Yes."

"And nobody lives in it? It has no door to it?"

"There ha'n't been anybody in it these seven years."

"I know the place very well," said the sergeant, thoughtfully , "there is woods just on this side of it."

"That's true," replied the dame. "But what is it you are thinking about, Mr. Robinson?"

"How long before this rain began was it that they quitted this house?"

"Not above fifteen minutes."

"Mrs. Ramsay, bring me the rifle and pistol, both — and the powderhorn and bullets."

"As you say, Mr. Horseshoe," answered the dame, as she turned round to leave the room; "but I am sure I can't suspicion what you mean to do."

In a few moments the woman returned with the weapons, and gave them to the sergeant.

"Where is Andy?" asked Horseshoe.

The hostess went to the door and called her son ; and almost immediately afterward a sturdy boy, of about twelve or fourteen years of age, entered the apartment, his clothes dripping with rain. He modestly and shyly seated himself on a chair near the door, with his soaked hat flapping down over a face full of freckles, and not less rife with the expression of an open, dauntless hardihood of character.

"How would you like a scrummage, Andy, with them

Scotchmen that stole your mother's chickens this morning ? " asked Horseshoe.

" I'm agreed," replied the boy, "if you will tell me what to do."

" You are not going to take the boy out on any of your desperate projects, Mr. Horseshoe ? " said the mother, with the tears starting instantly into her eyes. " You wouldn't take such a child as that into danger ! "

" Bless your soul, Mrs. Ramsay, there isn't any danger about it !   It's a thing that is either done at a blow, or not done ; and there's an end of it.   I want the lad only to bring home the prisoners for me, after I have taken them."

" Ah, Mr. Robinson, I have one son already in these wars — God protect him — and you men don't know how a mother's heart yearns for her children in these times.   I cannot give another," she added, as she threw her arms over the shoulders of the youth and drew him to her bosom.

" Oh, it isn't anything," said Andrew, in a sprightly tone.   " It's only snapping of a pistol, mother.   Pooh ! If I'm not afraid, you oughtn't to be."

" I give you my honor, Mrs. Ramsay," said Robinson, " that I will bring or send your son safe back in one hour, and that he sha'n't be put in any sort of danger whatsoever.   Come, that's a good woman ! "

" You are not deceiving me, Mr. Robinson ? " asked the matron, wiping away a tear.   " You wouldn't mock the sufferings of a weak woman in such a thing as this ? "

"On the honesty of a soldier, ma'am," replied Horseshoe, "the lad shall be in no danger, as I said before — whatsoever."

"Then I will say no more," answered the mother. "But, Andy, my child, be sure to let Mr. Robinson keep before you."

Horseshoe now loaded the firearms, and, having slung the pouch across his body, he put the pistol into the hands of the boy ; then, shouldering his rifle, he and his young ally left the room. . . .

"Now, Andy, my lad," said Horseshoe, after he had mounted his horse, " you must get up behind me.   Turn the lock of your pistol down," he continued, as the boy sprang upon the horse's back, " and cover it with the flap of your jacket, to keep the rain off.   It won't do to hang fire at such a time as this."

The lad did as he was directed, and Horseshoe, having secured his rifle in the same way, put his horse up to a gallop and took the road in the direction that had been pursued by the soldiers.

As soon as our adventurers had gained a wood, at the distance of about half a mile, the sergeant relaxed his speed and advanced at a pace a little above a walk.

"Andy," he said, " we have rather a ticklish sort of a job before us ; so I must give you your lesson, which you will understand better by knowing something of my plan.   As soon as your mother told me that these villains had left her house about fifteen minutes before the rain came on, and that they had gone along upon this road, I remembered the old field up here and

the little log hut in the middle of it; and it was natural
to suppose that they had just got about near that hut
when this rain came up; and then it was the most sup-
posable case in the world that they would naturally go
into it, as the driest place they could find. So now you
see it's my calculation that the whole batch is there at
this very point of time. We will go slowly along until
we get to the other end of this wood, in sight of the old
field; and then, if there is no one on the lookout, we
will open our first trench; you know what that means,
Andy?"

"It means, I suppose, that we'll go right at them,"
replied Andrew.

"Exactly," said the sergeant. "But listen to me.
Just at the edge of the woods you will have to get down
and put yourself behind a tree. I'll ride forward, as if
I had a whole troop at my heels; and if I catch them,
as I expect, they will have a little fire kindled, and, as
likely as not, they'll be cooking some of your mother's
fowls."

"Yes, I understand," said the boy, eagerly.

"No, you don't," replied Horseshoe; "but you will
when you hear what I am going to say. If I get at
them unawares they'll be very apt to think they are
surrounded, and will bellow like fine fellows for quarter. And thereupon, Andy, I'll cry out, 'Stand fast!'
as if I were speaking to my own men; and when you
hear that, you must come up at once — because it will
be a signal to you that the enemy has surrendered.
Then it will be your business to run into the house and

bring out the muskets as quick as a rat runs through a kitchen; and when you have done that — why all's done. But if you should hear any popping of firearms, — that is, more than one shot, which I may chance to let off, — do you take that for a bad sign, and get away as fast as you can heel it. You comprehend?"

"Oh, yes," replied the lad, "and I'll do what you want — and more too, maybe, Mr. Robinson."

"*Captain* Robinson, remember, Andy : you must call me captain, in the hearing of the Scotchmen."

"I'll not forget that, neither," answered Andrew.

By the time that these instructions were fully impressed upon the boy, our adventurous forlorn hope, as it may fitly be called, had arrived at the place which Horseshoe had designated for the commencement of active operations. They had a clear view of the old field, and it afforded them a strong assurance that the enemy was exactly where they wished him to be when they discovered smoke arising from the chimney of the hovel. Andrew was soon posted behind a tree, and Robinson only tarried a moment to make the boy repeat the signals agreed on, in order to ascertain that he had them correctly in his memory. Being satisfied from this experiment that the intelligence of his young companion might be depended upon, he galloped across the intervening space, and in a few seconds abruptly reined up his steed in the very doorway of the hut. The party within was gathered around a fire at the farther end ; and in the corner near the door were four muskets thrown together against the wall. To spring from his saddle and thrust himself one pace inside of the door was a movement which the sergeant executed in an instant, shouting at the same time : —

"Halt! File off right and left to both sides of the house, and wait orders. I demand the surrender of all here," he said, as he planted himself between the party and their weapons. "I will shoot down the first man who moves a foot."

"Leap to your arms!" cried the young officer who commanded the little party inside of the house. "Why do you stand?"

"I don't want to do you or your men any harm, young man," said Robinson, as he brought his rifle to a level, "but I will not leave one of you to be put upon a muster roll if you raise a hand at this moment!"

Both parties now stood for a brief space eying each other, in a fearful suspense, during which there was an expression of doubt and irresolution visible on the countenances of the soldiers as they surveyed the broad proportions and met the stern glance of the sergeant; while the delay, also, began to raise an apprehension in the mind of Robinson that his stratagem would be discovered.

"Shall I let loose upon them, captain?" said Andrew Ramsay, now appearing, most unexpectedly to Robinson, at the door of the hut. "Come on, boys!" he shouted, as he turned his face toward the field.

"Keep them outside of the door. Stand fast!" cried the doughty sergeant, with admirable promptitude, in the new and sudden posture of his affairs caused by this opportune appearance of the boy. "Sir, you see that it's not worth while fighting five to one; so take my advice, and surrender to the Continental Congress and this scrap of its army which I command."

During this appeal the sergeant was ably seconded by the lad outside, who was calling out first on one name and then on another, as if in the presence of a troop. The officer within, believing the forbearance of Robinson to be real, at length said: —

"Lower your rifle, sir. In the presence of a superior force, taken by surprise and without arms, it is my duty to save bloodshed. With the promise of fair usage and the rights of prisoners of war, I surrender this little foraging party under my command."

" I'll make the terms agreeable," replied the sergeant. "Never doubt me, sir. Right hand, file, advance, and receive the arms of the prisoners ! "

"I'm here, captain," said Andrew, in a conceited tone, as if it were a mere occasion of merriment; and the lad quickly entered the house and secured the weapons, retreating with them some paces from the door.

"Now, sir," said Horseshoe to the ensign, "your sword, and whatever else you may have about you of the ammunitions of war ! "

The officer delivered up his sword and a pair of pocket pistols.

As Horseshoe received these tokens of victory, he asked, with a lambent smile, and what he intended to be an elegant and condescending composure, "Your name? — if I may take the freedom."

"Ensign St. Jermyn, of his Majesty's Seventy-first Regiment of Light Infantry."

"Ensign, your servant," added Horseshoe, still preserving this unusual exhibition of politeness. "You have defended your post like an old soldier, although you haven't much beard on your chin; but seeing you have given up, you shall be treated like a man who has done his duty. You will walk out now, and form yourselves in line at the door. I'll engage my men shall do you no harm."

When the little squad of prisoners submitted to this command, and came to the door, they were stricken with equal astonishment and mortification to find, in place of the detachment of cavalry which they expected to see, nothing but a man, a boy, and a horse. Their first emotions were expressed in curses, which were even succeeded by laughter from one or two of the number. There seemed to be a disposition, on the part of some, to resist the authority that now controlled them, and sundry glances were exchanged which indicated a purpose to turn upon their captors. The sergeant no sooner perceived this than he halted, raised his rifle to his breast, and at the same instant gave Andrew Ramsay an order to retire a few paces and to fire one of the captured pieces at the first man who opened his lips.

"By my hand," he said, "if I find any trouble in taking you, all five, safe away from this house, I will thin your numbers with your own muskets! And that's as good as if I had sworn to it."

"You have my word, sir," said the ensign. "Lead on."

"By your leave, my pretty gentleman, you will lead, and I'll follow," replied Horseshoe. "It may be a new piece of drill to you, but the custom is to give the prisoners the post of honor."

Finding the conqueror determined to execute summary martial law upon the first who should mutiny, the prisoners submitted, and marched in double file from the hut back toward Ramsay's — followed by Horseshoe and his gallant young auxiliary, Andrew.

"Well, I have brought you your ducks and chickens back, mistress," said the sergeant, as he halted the prisoners at the door, "and, what's more, I have brought home a young soldier that's worth his weight in gold."

"Heaven bless my child! my boy, my brave boy!" cried the mother, seizing the lad in her arms, and unheeding anything else in the present perturbation of her feelings. "I feared ill would come of it; but Heaven has preserved him. Did he behave handsomely, Mr. Robinson? But I am sure he did."

"A little more venturesome, ma'am, than I wanted him to be," replied Horseshoe. "But he did excellent service. These are his prisoners, Mrs. Ramsay; I should never have taken them if it hadn't been for Andy. Show me another boy in America that's made more prisoners than there were men to fight them with — that's all!"

ARNOLD VON WINKELRIED

JAMES MONTGOMERY

"MAKE way for liberty!" he cried,
Made way for liberty, and died.
In arms the Austrian phalanx stood,
A living wall, a human wood, —
A wall, where every conscious stone
Seemed to its kindred thousands grown.
A rampart all assaults to bear,
Till time to dust their frames should wear:
So still, so dense the Austrians stood,
A living wall, a human wood.

Impregnable their front appears,
All horrent with projected spears,
Whose polished points before them shine,
From flank to flank, one brilliant line,
Bright as the breakers' splendors run
Along the billows to the sun.

Opposed to these a hovering band
Contended for their fatherland;
Peasants, whose new-found strength had broke
From manly necks the ignoble yoke,
And beat their fetters into swords,
On equal terms to fight their lords;
And what insurgent rage had gained,
In many a mortal fray maintained;

Marshaled, once more, at Freedom's call,
They came to conquer or to fall,
Where he who conquered, he who fell,
Was deemed a dead or living Tell.
Such virtue had that patriot breathed,
So to the soil his soul bequeathed,
That wheresoe'er his arrows flew,
Heroes in his own likeness grew,
And warriors sprang from every sod,
Which his awakening footstep trod.
And now the work of life and death
Hung on the passing of a breath;
The fire of conflict burned within,
The battle trembled to begin;
Yet, while the Austrians held their ground,
Point for attack was nowhere found;
Where'er the impatient Switzers gazed,
The unbroken line of lances blazed;
That line 'twere suicide to meet,
And perish at their tyrant's feet;
How could they rest within their graves,
And leave their homes the homes of slaves?
Would not they feel their children tread,
With clanging chains, above their head?

It must not be; this day, this hour,
Annihilates the invader's power;
All Switzerland is in the field;
She will not fly, — she cannot yield, —
She must not fall; her better fate

Here gives her an immortal date.
Few were the numbers she could boast,
But every freeman was a host,
And felt as 'twere a secret known
That one should turn the scale alone,
While each unto himself was he
On whose sole arm hung victory.

It did depend on one indeed;
Behold him, — Arnold Winkelried;
There sounds not to the trump of fame
The echo of a nobler name.
Unmarked he stood amidst the throng,
In rumination deep and long,
Till you might see, with sudden grace,
The very thought come o'er his face;
And, by the motion of his form,
Anticipate the bursting storm,
And, by the uplifting of his brow,
Tell where the bolt would strike, and how.

But 'twas no sooner thought than done!
The field was in a moment won;
" Make way for liberty! " he cried,
Then ran, with arms extended wide,
As if his dearest friend to clasp;
Ten spears he swept within his grasp;
" Make way for liberty ! " he cried.
Their keen points crossed from side to side;
He bowed amidst them like a tree,
And thus made way for liberty.

Swift to the breach his comrades fly,
" Make way for liberty ! " they cry,
And through the Austrian phalanx dart,
As rushed the spears through Arnold's heart,
While instantaneous as his fall,
Rout, ruin, panic seized them all ;
An earthquake could not overthrow
A city with a surer blow.

Thus Switzerland again was free ;
Thus Death made way for Liberty !

THE SPANIARDS' RETREAT FROM MEXICO

William Hickling Prescott

There was no longer any question as to the ex-
pediency of evacuating the capital. The only doubt
was as to the time of doing so, and the route. The
Spanish commander called a council of officers to de-
liberate on these matters. It was his purpose to
retreat on Tlascala, and in that capital to decide,
according to circumstances, on his future operations.
After some discussion they agreed on the causeway
of Tlacopan as the avenue by which to leave the
city. It would, indeed, take them back by a cir-
cuitous route, considerably longer than either of those
by which they had approached the capital. But for
that reason it would be less likely to be guarded, as
least suspected ; and the causeway itself, being shorter

than either of the other entrances, would sooner place
the army in comparative security on the mainland.

The general's first care was to provide for the safe
transportation of the treasure. Many of the common
soldiers had converted their share of the prize into
gold chains, collars, or other ornaments, which they
easily carried about their persons. But the royal
fifth, together with that of Cortés himself, had been
converted into bars and wedges of solid gold, and
deposited in one of the strong apartments of the palace. Cortés delivered the share belonging to the
Crown to the royal officers, assigning them one of
the strongest horses and a guard of Castilian soldiers
to transport it. Still much of the treasure, belonging
both to the Crown and to individuals, was necessarily
abandoned, from the want of adequate means of con-
veyance. The metal lay scattered in shining heaps
along the floor, exciting the cupidity of the soldiers.
" Take what you will of it," said Cortés to his men.
" Better you should have it than these Mexican
hounds. But be careful not to overload yourselves.
He travels safest in the dark night who travels
lightest." . . .

The general had already superintended the construc-
tion of a portable bridge to be laid over the open canals
in the causeway. This was given in charge to an officer named Magarino, with forty soldiers under his
orders, all pledged to defend the passage to the last
extremity. The bridge was to be taken up when the
entire army had crossed one of the breaches, and trans-

ported to the next. There were three of these openings in the causeway, and most fortunate would it have been for the expedition if the foresight of the commander had provided the same number of bridges. But the labor would have been great, and the time was short.

At midnight the troops were under arms, in readiness for the march. Mass was performed by Father Olmedo, who invoked the protection of the Almighty through the awful perils of the night. The gates were thrown open, and on the 1st of July, 1520, the Spaniards for the last time sallied forth from the walls of the ancient fortress, the scene of so much suffering and such indomitable courage.

The night was cloudy, and a drizzling rain, which fell without intermission, added to the obscurity. The great square before the palace was deserted, as, indeed, it had been since the fall of Montezuma. Steadily, and as noiselessly as possible, the Spaniards held their way along the great street of Tlacopan, which so lately had resounded with the tumult of battle. All was now hushed in silence, and they were only reminded of the past by the occasional presence of some solitary corpse or a dark heap of the slain, which too plainly told where the strife had been hottest. As they passed along the lanes and alleys which opened into the great street, or looked down the canals, whose polished surface gleamed with a sort of ebon luster through the obscurity of night, they easily fancied that they discerned the shadowy forms of their foe lurking in ambush and ready to spring upon them. But it was only fancy ; and the city slept undisturbed even by the prolonged echoes of the tramp of the horses and the hoarse rumbling of the artillery and baggage trains. At length a lighter space beyond the dusky line of buildings showed the van of the army that it was emerging on the open causeway. They might well have congratulated themselves on having thus escaped the dangers of an assault in the city itself, and that a brief time would place them in comparative safety on the opposite shore. But the Mexicans were not all asleep.

As the Spaniards drew near the spot where the street opened on the causeway, and were preparing to lay the portable bridge across the uncovered breach, which now met their eyes, several Indian sentinels, who had been stationed at this, as at the other approaches to the city, took the alarm and fled, rousing their countrymen by their cries. The priests, keeping their night watch on the summit of the *teocallis*, instantly caught the tidings and sounded their shells, while the huge drum in the desolate temple of the war god sent forth those solemn tones which, heard only in seasons of calamity, vibrated through every corner of the capital. The Spaniards saw that no time was to be lost. The bridge was brought forward and fitted with all possible expedition. Sandoval was the first to try its strength, and, riding across, was followed by his little body of cavalry, his infantry, and Tlascalan allies, who formed the first division of the army. Then came Cortés and his squadrons, with the baggage, ammunition wagons, and a part of the artillery. But before they had time to defile across the narrow passage, a gathering sound was heard, like that of a mighty forest agitated by the winds. It grew louder and louder, while on the dark waters of the lake was heard a plashing noise, as of many oars. Then came a few stones and arrows striking at random among the hurrying troops. They fell every moment faster and more furious, till they thickened into a terrible tempest, while the very heavens were rent with the yells and war cries of myriads of combatants, who seemed all at once to be swarming over land and lake.

The Spaniards pushed steadily on through this arrowy sleet, though the barbarians, dashing their canoes against the sides of the causeway, clambered up and broke in upon their ranks. But the Christians, anxious only to make their escape, declined all combat except for self-preservation. The cavaliers, spurring forward their steeds, shook off their assailants and rode over their prostrate bodies, while the men on foot, with their good swords or the butts of their pieces, drove them headlong again down the sides of the dike.

But the advance of several thousand men, marching, probably, on a front of not more than fifteen or twenty abreast, necessarily required much time, and the leading files had already reached the second breach in the causeway before those in the rear had entirely traversed the first. Here they halted, as they had no means of effecting a passage, smarting all the while under the unintermitting volleys from the enemy, who were clustered thick on the waters around this second opening. Sorely distressed, the vanguard sent repeated messages to the rear to demand the portable bridge. At length the last of the army had crossed, and Magarino and his sturdy followers endeavored to raise the ponderous framework. But it stuck fast in the sides of the dike. In vain they strained every nerve. The weight of so many men and horses, and, above all, of the heavy artillery, had wedged the timbers so firmly in the stones and earth that it was beyond their power to dislodge them. Still they labored amid a torrent of missiles, until, many of them slain, and all wounded, they were obliged to abandon the attempt.

The tidings soon spread from man to man, and no sooner was their dreadful import comprehended than a cry of despair arose, which for a moment drowned all the noise of conflict. All means of retreat were cut off. Scarcely hope was left. The only hope was in such desperate exertions as each could make for himself. Order and subordination were at an end. Intense danger produced intense selfishness. Each thought only of his own life. Pressing forward, he trampled down the weak and the wounded, heedless whether it were friend or foe. The leading files, urged on by the rear, were crowded on the brink of the gulf. Sandoval, Ordaz, and the other cavaliers dashed into the water. Some succeeded in swimming their horses across. Others failed, and some, who reached the opposite bank, being overturned in the ascent, rolled headlong with their steeds into the lake. The infantry

followed pellmell, heaped promiscuously on one another, frequently pierced by the shafts or struck down
by the war clubs of the Aztecs ; while many an unfortunate victim was dragged half stunned on board their
canoes, to be reserved for a protracted but more dreadful death.

The carnage raged fearfully along the length of the
causeway. Its shadowy bulk presented a mark of
sufficient distinctness for the enemy's missiles, which
often prostrated their own countrymen in the blind
fury of the tempest. Those nearest the dike, running
their canoes alongside, with a force that shattered them
to pieces, leaped on the land, and grappled with the Christians, until both came rolling down the sides of the causeway together. But the Aztec fell among his friends,
while his antagonist was borne away in triumph to the
sacrifice. The struggle was long and deadly. The
Mexicans were recognized by their white cotton
tunics, which showed faint through the darkness.
Above the combatants rose a wild and discordant
clamor, in which horrid shouts of vengeance were
mingled with groans of agony, with invocations of
the saints and the blessed Virgin, and with the screams
of women ; for there were several women, both natives
and Spaniards, who had accompanied the Christian
camp.

The opening in the causeway, meanwhile, was filled
up with the wreck of matter which had been forced
into it, — ammunition wagons, heavy guns, bales of rich
stuffs scattered over the waters, chests of solid ingots,

and bodies of men and horses, — till over this dismal ruin a passage was gradually formed, by which those in the rear were enabled to clamber to the other side. Cortés, it is said, found a place that was fordable, where, halting, with the water up to his saddle girths, he endeavored to check the confusion, and lead his followers by a safer path to the opposite bank. But his voice was lost in the wild uproar, and finally, hurrying on with the tide, he pressed forward with a few trusty cavaliers, who remained near his person, to the van. Here he found Sandoval and his companions halting before the third and last breach, endeavoring to cheer on their followers to surmount it. But their resolution faltered. It was wide and deep, though the passage was not so closely beset by the enemy as the preceding ones. The cavaliers again set the example by plunging into the water. Horse and foot followed as they could, some swimming, others with dying grasp clinging to the manes and tails of the struggling animals. Those fared best, as the general had predicted, who traveled lightest ; and many were the unfortunate wretches who, weighed down by the fatal gold which they loved so well, were buried with it in the salt floods of the lake. Cortés, with his gallant comrades, still kept in the advance, leading his broken remnant off the fatal causeway. The din of battle lessened in the distance ; when the rumor reached them that the rear guard would be wholly overwhelmed without speedy relief. It seemed almost an act of desperation ; but the generous hearts of the Spanish cavaliers did not stop to calculate danger when the cry for succor reached them. Turning their horses' bridles, they galloped back to the theater of action, worked their way through the press, swam the canal, and placed themselves in the thick of the *mêlée* on the opposite bank.

The first gray of the morning was now coming over the waters. It showed the hideous confusion of the scene which had been shrouded in the obscurity of night. The dark masses of combatants, stretching along the dike, were seen struggling for mastery, until the very causeway on which they stood appeared to tremble, and reel to and fro, as if shaken by an earthquake ; while the bosom of the lake, as far as the eye could reach, was darkened by canoes crowded with warriors, whose spears and bludgeons, armed with blades of " volcanic glass," gleamed in the morning light.

The artillery, in the earlier part of the engagement, had not been idle, and its iron shower, sweeping along the dike, had mowed down the assailants, then in possession of the rear of the causeway, by hundreds. But nothing could resist their impetuosity. The front ranks, pushed on by those behind, were at length forced up to the pieces, and, pouring over them like a torrent, overthrew men and guns in one general ruin. The resolute charge of the Spanish cavaliers, who had now arrived, created a temporary check, and gave time for their countrymen to make a feeble rally. But they were speedily borne down by the returning flood. Cortés and his companions were compelled to plunge again into the lake — though all did not escape. They rode forward to the front, where the troops, in a loose, disorderly manner, were marching off the fatal causeway. A few only of the enemy hung on their rear, or annoyed them by occasional flights of arrows from the lake. The attention of the Aztecs was diverted by the rich spoil that strewed the battle ground ; fortunately for the Spaniards, who, had their enemy pursued with the same ferocity with which he had fought, would, in their crippled condition, have been cut off, probably to a man. But little molested, therefore, they were allowed to defile through the adjacent village, or suburbs it might be called, of Popotla.

The Spanish commander then dismounted from his jaded steed, and sitting down on the steps of an Indian temple, gazed mournfully on the broken files as they passed before him. What a spectacle did they present ! The cavalry, most of them dismounted, were mingled with the infantry, who dragged their feeble limbs along with difficulty; their shattered mail and tattered garments dripping with the salt ooze, showing through their rents many a bruise and ghastly wound ; their bright arms soiled, their proud crests and banners gone, the baggage, artillery — all, in short, that constitutes the pride and panoply of glorious war — forever lost. Cortés, as he looked wistfully on their thin and disordered ranks, sought in vain for many a familiar face, and missed more than one dear companion who had stood side by side with him through all the perils of the conquest. Though accustomed to control his emotions, or, at least, to conceal them, the sight was too much for him. He covered his face with his hands, and the tears which trickled down too plainly showed the anguish of his soul.

CONCORD HYMN

SUNG AT THE COMPLETION OF THE BATTLE MONUMENT, APRIL 19, 1836

RALPH WALDO EMERSON

By the rude bridge that arched the flood,
　　Their flag to April's breeze unfurled,
Here once the embattled farmers stood,
　　And fired the shot heard round the world.

The foe long since in silence slept;
　　Alike the conqueror silent sleeps;
And Time the ruined bridge has swept
　　Down the dark stream which seaward creeps.

On this green bank, by this soft stream,
　　We set to-day a votive stone;
That memory may their deed redeem,
　　When, like our sires, our sons are gone.

Spirit, that made those heroes dare
　　To die, and leave their children free,
Bid Time and Nature gently spare
　　The shaft we raise to them and thee.

ONE NICHE THE HIGHEST

Elihu Burritt

THE scene opens with a view of the great Natural Bridge in Virginia. There are three or four lads standing in the channel below, looking up with awe to that vast arch of unhewn rocks which the Almighty bridged over those everlasting butments " when the morning stars sang together." The little piece of sky spanning those measureless piers is full of stars, although it is midday. It is almost five hundred feet from where they stand, up those perpendicular bulwarks of limestone to the key of that vast arch, which appears to them only of the size of a man's hand. The silence of death is rendered more impressive by the little stream that falls from rock to rock down the channel. The sun is darkened, and the boys have uncovered their heads, as if standing in the presence-chamber of the Majesty of the whole earth. At last this feeling begins to wear away ; they look around them, and find that others have been there before them. They see the names of hundreds cut in the limestone butments. A new feeling comes over their young hearts, and their knives are in their hands in an instant. " What man has done, man can do," is their watchword, while they draw themselves up, and carve their names a foot above those of a hundred full-grown men who have been there before them.

They are all satisfied with this feat of physical exertion, except one. This ambitious youth sees a name just above his reach — a name which will be green in the memory of the world when those of Alexander, Cæsar, and Bonaparte shall rot in oblivion. It was the name of Washington. Before he marched with Braddock to that fatal field, he had been there and left his name a foot above that of any of his predecessors. It was a glorious thought to write his name side by side with that of the Father of his Country. He grasps his knife with a firmer hand, and, clinging to a little jutting crag, he cuts a niche into the limestone, about a foot above where he stands; he then reaches up and cuts another for his hands. 'Tis a dangerous adventure; and, as he draws himself up carefully to his full length, he finds himself a foot above every name chronicled in that mighty wall. While his companions are regarding him with concern and admiration, he cuts his name in wide capitals, large and deep, into that flinty album. His knife is still in his hand, and strength in his sinews, and a new-created aspiration in his heart. Again he cuts another niche, and again he carves his name in larger capitals. This is not enough; heedless of the entreaties of his companions, he cuts and climbs again. He measures his length at every gain he cuts. The voices of his friends wax weaker and weaker, till their words are finally lost on his ear. He now for the first time casts a look beneath him. Had that glance lasted a moment more, that moment would have been his last. He clings with a convulsive shudder to his little niche in the rock. His knife is worn halfway to the haft.

There is no retracing his steps. It is impossible to put his hands into the same niche with his feet and retain his slender hold a moment. He is too high to ask for his father and mother, his brothers and sisters. But one of his companions anticipates his desire. Swift as the wind he bounds down the channel, and the situation of the fated boy is told upon his father's hearthstone.

Minutes of almost eternal length roll on, and there are hundreds standing in that rocky channel and hundreds on the bridge above, all holding their breath, and awaiting the fearful catastrophe. The poor boy hears the hum of new and numerous voices, both above and below. He can just distinguish the tones of his father, who is shouting with all the energy of despair: "William! William! don't look down! Your mother, and Henry and Harriet are all here praying for you! Don't look down! Keep your eyes toward the top!" The boy didn't look down. He cuts another niche, and another foot is added to the hundreds that remove him from the reach of human help from below. How carefully he uses his wasting blade! How anxiously he selects the softest places in that vast pier! How he avoids every flinty grain! How every motion is watched from below! There stand his father, mother, brother, and sister on the very spot where, if he falls, he will not fall alone.

The sun is halfway down in the west. The lad has made fifty additional niches in that mighty wall. Fifty more must be cut before the longest rope can reach him. His wasting blade strikes again into the limestone. The boy is emerging painfully, foot by foot, from under that lofty arch. Spliced ropes are ready in the hands of those who are leaning over the outer edge of the bridge above. The boy's head reels; his eyes are starting from their sockets. His life must hang on the next gain he cuts. That niche is his last.

At the last faint gash he makes, his knife — his faithful knife — falls from his little, nerveless hand, and ringing along the precipice, falls at his mother's feet. An involuntary groan of despair runs like a death knell through the channel below, and all is as still as the grave. At the height of nearly three hundred feet the devoted boy lifts his hopeless heart, and closes his eyes to commend his soul to God.

'Tis but a moment — there! one foot swings off — he is reeling — trembling — toppling over into eternity! Hark! a shout falls on his ear from above! The man who is lying with half his length over the bridge, has caught a glimpse of the boy's head and shoulders. Quick as thought the noosed rope is within reach of the sinking youth. With a faint, convulsive effort the swooning boy drops his arms into the noose. Darkness comes over him, and with the words " God — mother "— whispered on his lips — the tightening rope lifts him out of his last shallow niche. Not a lip moves while he is dangling over that fearful abyss ; but when a sturdy Virginian reaches down and draws up the lad, such shouting — such weeping and leaping for joy — never greeted the ear of a human being so recovered from the yawning gulf of eternity.

THE SCHOOL AT DOTHEBOYS HALL

CHARLES DICKENS

A RIDE of two hundred and odd miles in severe weather is one of the best softeners of a hard bed that ingenuity can devise. Perhaps it is even a sweetener of dreams, for those which hovered over the rough couch of Nicholas, and whispered their airy nothings in his ear, were of an agreeable and happy kind. He was making his fortune very fast indeed, when the faint glimmer of an expiring candle shone before his eyes, and a voice he had no difficulty in recognizing as part and parcel of Mr. Squeers admonished him that it was time to rise.

"Past seven, Nickleby," said Mr. Squeers.

"Has morning come already?" asked Nicholas, sitting up in bed.

"Ah! that has it," replied Squeers, "and ready iced, too. Now, Nickleby, come; tumble up, will you?"

Nicholas needed no further admonition, but "tumbled up" at once, and proceeded to dress himself by the light of the taper which Mr. Squeers carried in his hand.

"Here's a pretty go," said that gentleman; "the pump's froze!"

"Indeed!" said Nicholas, not much interested in the intelligence.

"Yes," replied Squeers. "You can't wash yourself this morning."

"Not wash myself!" exclaimed Nicholas.

" No, not a bit of it," rejoined Squeers, tartly. " So you must be content with giving yourself a dry polish till we break the ice in the well and get a bucketful out for the boys. Don't stand staring at me, but do look sharp, will you? "

Offering no further observation, Nicholas huddled on his clothes. Squeers, meanwhile, opened the shutters and blew the candle out ; when the voice of his amiable consort was heard in the passage, demanding admittance.

" I can't find the school spoon anywhere," said Mrs. Squeers.

" Never mind it, my dear," observed Squeers, in a soothing manner ; " it's of no consequence."

" No consequence ? why, how you talk ! " retorted Mrs. Squeers, sharply ; " isn't it brimstone morning? "

" I forgot, my dear," rejoined Squeers ; " yes, it certainly is. We purify the boys' blood now and then, Nickleby."

" Purify fiddle-sticks' ends ! " said his lady. " Don't think, young man, that we go to the expense of flowers of brimstone and molasses just to purify them ; because if you think we carry on business that way, you'll find yourself mistaken, and so I tell you plainly."

" My dear ! " said Squeers, frowning. " Hem ! "

" Oh, nonsense ! " rejoined Mrs. Squeers. " If the young man comes to be a teacher here, let him understand at once that we don't want any foolery about the boys. They have the brimstone and treacle, partly because if they hadn't something or other in the way of medicine they'd be always ailing and giving a world

into a bare and dirty room, with a couple of windows,
whereof a tenth part might be of glass, the remainder
being stopped up with old copy books and paper.
There were a couple of long, old, rickety desks, cut
and notched and inked, and damaged in every possible way; two or three forms; a detached desk for
Squeers, and another for his assistant. The ceiling
was supported, like that of a barn, by crossbeams
and rafters; and the walls were so stained and dis-
colored that it was impossible to tell whether they
had ever been touched with paint or whitewash.

But the pupils — the young noblemen! How the
last faint traces of hope, the remotest glimmering of
any good to be derived from his efforts in this den,
faded from the mind of Nicholas as he looked in dis-
may around! Pale and haggard faces, lank and bony
figures, children with the countenances of old men,
deformities with irons upon their limbs, boys of
stunted growth, and others, whose long meager legs
would hardly bear their stooping bodies, all crowded
on the view together. There were the bleared eye,
the harelip, the crooked foot, and every ugliness or
distortion that told of unnatural aversion conceived
by parents for their offspring, or of young lives which,
from the earliest dawn of infancy, had been one hor-
rible endurance of cruelty and neglect. There were
little faces, which should have been handsome, darkened with the scowl of sullen, dogged suffering; there
was childhood with the light of its eye quenched, its
beauty gone, and its helplessness alone remaining;

there were vicious-faced boys, brooding with leaden eyes, like malefactors in a jail; and there were young creatures on whom the sins of their frail parents had descended, weeping even for the mercenary nurses they had known, and lonesome even in their loneliness. With every kindly sympathy and affection blasted in its birth, with every young and healthy feeling flogged and starved down, with every revengeful passion that can fester in swollen hearts eating its evil way to their core in silence, what an incipient hell was breeding here!

And yet this scene, painful as it was, had its grotesque features, which, in a less interested observer than Nicholas, might have provoked a smile. Mrs. Squeers stood at one of the desks, presiding over an immense basin of brimstone and treacle, of which delicious compound she administered a large installment to each boy in succession; using for the purpose a common wooden spoon, which might have been originally manufactured for some gigantic top, and which widened every young gentleman's mouth considerably; they being all obliged, under heavy corporal penalties, to take in the whole of the bowl at a gasp. In another corner, huddled together for companionship, were the little boys who had arrived the preceding night, three of them in very large leather breeches, and two in old trousers. At no great distance from these was seated the juvenile son and heir of Mr. Squeers — a striking likeness of his father — kicking with great vigor under the hands of Smike,

who was fitting upon him a pair of new boots that
bore a most suspicious resemblance to those which
the least of the little boys had worn on the journey
down — as the little boy himself seemed to think, for
he was regarding the appropriation with a look of
most rueful amazement. Besides these there was a
long row of boys waiting, with countenances of no
pleasant anticipation, to be treacled; and another file,
who had just escaped from the infliction, making a
variety of wry mouths indicative of anything but
satisfaction. The whole were attired in such motley,
ill-assorted, extraordinary garments as would have
been irresistibly ridiculous but for the foul appearance of dirt, disorder, and disease with which they
were associated.

"Now," said Squeers, giving the desk a great rap
with his cane, which made half the little boys nearly
jump out of their boots, "is that physicking over?"

"Just over," said Mrs. Squeers, choking the last
boy in her hurry, and tapping the crown of his head
with the wooden spoon to restore him. "Here, you
Smike, take that away now. Look sharp!"

Smike shuffled out with the basin; and Mrs. Squeers
having called up a little boy with a curly head and
wiped her hands upon it, hurried out after him into
a species of washhouse, where there was a small fire
and a large kettle, together with a number of little
wooden bowls which were arranged upon a board.
Into these bowls Mrs. Squeers, assisted by the hungry
servant, poured a brown composition, which looked

like diluted pincushions without the covers, and was called porridge.

A minute wedge of brown bread was inserted in each bowl, and when the boys had eaten their porridge by means of the bread, they ate the bread itself, and had finished their breakfast; whereupon Mr. Squeers said, in a solemn voice, " For what we have received may the Lord make us truly thankful ! " and went away to his own.

Nicholas distended his stomach with a bowl of porridge, for much the same reason which induces some savages to swallow earth — lest they should be inconveniently hungry when there is nothing to eat. Having further disposed of a slice of bread and butter, allotted to him in virtue of his office, he sat himself down to wait for school time.

He could not but observe how silent and sad the boys all seemed to be. There was none of the noise and clamor of a schoolroom ; none of its boisterous play or hearty mirth. The children sat crouching and shivering together, and seemed to lack the spirit to move about. The only pupil who evinced the slightest tendency toward locomotion or playfulness was Master Squeers, and as his chief amusement was to tread upon the other boys' toes in his new boots, his flow of spirits was rather disagreeable than otherwise.

After some half hour's delay Mr. Squeers reappeared, and the boys took their places and their books, of which latter commodity the average might be about one to eight learners. A few minutes having elapsed, during

which Mr. Squeers looked very profound, as if he had a
perfect apprehension of what was inside all the books,
and could say every word of their contents by heart if
he only chose to take the trouble, that gentleman called
up the first class.

Obedient to this summons there ranged themselves
in front of the schoolmaster's desk half a dozen scare-
crows, out at knees and elbows, one of whom placed a
torn and filthy book beneath his learned eye.

"This is the first class in English spelling and philosophy, Nickleby," said Squeers, beckoning Nicholas
to stand beside him. "We'll get up a Latin one, and
hand that over to you. Now, then, where's the first
boy?"

"Please, sir, he's cleaning the back parlor window,"
said the temporary head of the philosophical class.

"So he is, to be sure," rejoined Squeers. "We go
upon the practical mode of teaching, Nickleby, — the
regular education system. C-l-e-a-n, clean, verb active
— to make bright, to scour. W-i-n, win, d-e-r, der, win-
der — a casement. When the boy knows this out of
book he goes and does it. It's just the same principle as the use of the globes. Where's the second
boy?"

"Please, sir, he's weeding the garden," replied a
small voice.

"To be sure," said Squeers, by no means disconcerted;
"so he is. B-o-t, bot, t-i-n, tin, bottin, n-e-y, ney, bottinney, noun substantive — a knowledge of plants. When
he has learned that bottinney means a knowledge of

plants, he goes and knows 'em. That's our system, Nickleby ; what do you think of it ? "

" It's a very useful one, at any rate," answered Nicholas.

" I believe you," rejoined Squeers, not remarking the emphasis of his usher.   " Third boy, what's a horse ? "

" A beast, sir," replied the boy.

" So it is," said Squeers.   " Ain't it, Nickleby ? "

" I believe there is no doubt of that, sir," answered Nicholas.

" Of course there isn't," said Squeers.   " A horse is a quadruped, and quadruped's Latin for beast, as everybody that's gone through the grammar knows, or else where's the use of having grammars at all ? "

" Where, indeed ? " said Nicholas, abstractedly.

" As you're perfect in that," resumed Squeers, turning to the boy, " go and look after *my* horse, and rub him down well, or I'll rub you down. The rest of the class go and draw water up till somebody tells you to leave off, for it's washing-day to-morrow, and they want the coppers filled."

So saying, he dismissed the first class to their experiments in practical philosophy, and eyed Nicholas with a look, half cunning and half doubtful, as if he were not altogether certain what he might think of him by this time.

" That's the way we do it, Nickleby," he said, after a pause.

Nicholas shrugged his shoulders in a manner that was scarcely perceptible, and said he saw it was.

"And a very good way it is too," said Squeers.
"Now, just take them fourteen little boys and hear
them some reading, because, you know, you must begin
to be useful.   Idling about here won't do."

Mr. Squeers said this as if it had suddenly occurred to
him either that he must not say too much to his assistant, or that his assistant did not say enough to him
in praise of the establishment.   The children were
arranged in a semicircle round the new master, and he
was soon listening to their dull, drawling, hesitating
recital of those stories of engrossing interest which are
to be found in the more antiquated spelling books.

— From "Nicholas Nickleby."

THE BURIAL OF MOSES

MRS. CECIL FRANCES ALEXANDER

By Nebo's lonely mountain,
　　On this side Jordan's wave,
In a vale in the land of Moab,
　　There lies a lonely grave ;
And no man knows that sepulcher,
　　And no man saw it e'er,
For the angels of God upturned the sod,
　　And laid the dead man there.

That was the grandest funeral
　　That ever passed on earth ;

Michelangelo, Sculptor.

STATUE OF MOSES.

But no man heard the trampling,
  Or saw the train go forth, —
Noiselessly as the daylight
  Comes back when night is done,
And the crimson streak on ocean's cheek
  Grows into the great sun, —

Noiselessly as the springtime
  Her crown of verdure weaves,
And all the trees on all the hills
  Open their thousand leaves ;
So without sound of music,
  Or voice of them that wept,
Silently down from the mountain's crown
  The great procession swept.

Perchance the bald old eagle,
  On gray Beth-peor's height,
Out of his lonely eyrie,
  Looked on the wondrous sight :
Perchance the lion stalking
  Still shuns that hallowed spot,
For beast and bird have seen and heard
  That which man knoweth not.

But when the warrior dieth,
  His comrades in the war,
With arms reversed and muffled drum,
  Follow his funeral car :
They show the banners taken,
  They tell his battles won,

And after him lead his masterless steed,
    While peals the minute gun.

Amid the noblest of the land
    We lay the sage to rest,
And give the bard an honored place,
    With costly marble drest,
In the great minster transept
    Where lights like glories fall,
And the organ rings, and the sweet choir sings,
    Along the emblazoned wall.

This was the truest warrior
    That ever buckled sword, —
This the most gifted poet
    That ever breathed a word;
And never earth's philosopher
    Traced with his golden pen,
On the deathless page, truths half so sage
    As he wrote down for men.

And had he not high honor —
    The hillside for a pall, —
To lie in state while angels wait,
    With stars for tapers tall, —
And the dark rock pines, like tossing plumes,
    Over his bier to wave,
And God's own hand in that lonely land,
    To lay him in the grave?

In that strange grave without a name,
    Whence his uncoffined clay

Behold, then, in 1673, on the tenth day of June, James Marquette and Louis Joliet, five Frenchmen as companions, and two Algonquins as guides, dragging their two canoes across the narrow portage that divides the Fox River from the Wisconsin. They reach the watershed ; uttering a special prayer to the immaculate Virgin, they leave the streams that could have borne their greetings to the castle of Quebec. " The guides returned," says the gentle Marquette, "leaving us alone, in this unknown land, in the hands of Providence." Embarking on the broad Wisconsin, the discoverers went solitarily down its current, between alternate plains and hillsides, beholding neither man nor familiar beasts : no sound broke the silence but the ripple of their canoes and the lowing of the buffalo. In seven days " they entered happily the Great River, with a joy that could not be expressed," and, raising their sails under new skies and to unknown breezes, floated down the calm magnificence of the ocean stream, over the broad, clear sand bars, the resort of innumerable waterfowl, through clusters of islets tufted with massive thickets, and between the natural parks of Illinois and Iowa. About sixty leagues below the Wisconsin the western bank of the Mississippi bore on its sands the trail of men ; a little footpath was discovered leading into beautiful fields ; and, leaving the canoes, Joliet and Marquette resolved alone to brave a meeting with the savages. After walking six miles, they beheld a village on the banks of a river, and two others on a slope, at a distance of a mile and a

half from the first. The river was the Moingona, of
which we have corrupted the name into Des Moines.
Marquette and Joliet, the first white men who trod the
soil of Iowa, commending themselves to God, uttered
a loud cry. Four old men advanced slowly to meet
them, bearing the peace pipe brilliant with many
colored plumes. "We are Illinois," said they — that
is, when translated, "We are men"; and they offered
the calumet. An aged chief received them at his
cabin with upraised hands, exclaiming : " How beautiful is the sun, Frenchman, when thou comest to visit
us ! Our whole village awaits thee ; thou shalt enter
in peace into our dwelling." And the pilgrims were
followed by the devouring gaze of an astonished
crowd.

To the council Marquette published the one true God,
their Creator. He spoke, also, of the great captain of
the French, the governor of Canada, who had chastised
the Five Nations and commanded peace ; and he ques-
tioned them respecting the Mississippi and the tribes
that possessed its banks. For the messengers, who
announced the subjection of the Iroquois, a magnificent festival was prepared of hominy and fish and the
choicest viands from the prairies.

After six days' delay, and invitations to new visits,
the chieftain of the tribe, with hundreds of warriors,
attended the strangers to their canoes ; and, selecting
a peace pipe embellished with the head and neck of
brilliant birds, and all feathered over with plumage of
various hues, they hung round Marquette the sacred

calumet, the mysterious arbiter of peace and war, a safeguard among the nations.

The little group proceeded onward. " I did not fear death," says Marquette, in July ; " I should have esteemed it the greatest happiness to have died for the glory of God." They passed the perpendicular rocks, which wore the appearance of monsters ; they heard at a distance the noise of the waters of the Missouri, known to them by its Algonquin name of Pekitanoni ; and, when they came to the grandest confluence of rivers in the world, — where the swifter Missouri rushes like a conqueror into the calmer Mississippi, dragging it, as it were, hastily to the sea, — the good Marquette resolved in his heart one day to ascend the mighty river to its source ; to cross the ridge that divides the oceans, and, descending a westerly flowing stream, to publish the gospel to all the people of this New World.

In a little less than forty leagues, the canoes floated past the Ohio, which was then, and long afterward, called the Wabash. Its banks were tenanted by numerous villages of the peaceful Shawnees, who quailed under the incursions of the Iroquois.

The thick canes begin to appear so close and strong that the buffalo could not break through them ; the insects become intolerable; as a shelter against the suns of July, the sails are folded into an awning. The prairies vanish; and forests of whitewood, admirable for their vastness and height, crowd even to the skirts of the pebbly shore. It is also observed that, in the land of the Chickasaws, the Indians have guns.

Near the latitude of thirty-three degrees, on the western bank of the Mississippi, stood the village of Mitchigamea in a region that had not been visited by Europeans since the days of De Soto. " Now," thought Marquette, " we must, indeed, ask the aid of the Virgin." Armed with bows and arrows, with clubs, axes, and bucklers, amid continual whoops, the natives embark in boats made out of the trunks of huge hollow trees ; but, at the sight of the mysterious peace pipe held aloft, they threw down their bows and quivers and prepared a hospitable welcome.

The next day, a long wooden canoe, containing ten men, escorted the discoverers, for eight or ten leagues, to the village of Akansea, the limit of their voyage. They had left the region of the Algonquins, and, in the midst of the Dakotas and Chickasaws, could speak only by an interpreter. A half league above Akansea, they were met by two boats, in one of which stood the commander, holding in his hand the peace pipe, and singing as he drew near. After offering the pipe, he gave bread of maize. The wealth of his tribe consisted in buffalo skins ; their weapons were axes of steel — a proof of commerce with Europeans.

Having descended below the entrance of the Arkansas, and having become certain that the father of rivers went not to the Gulf of California, but undoubtedly pours its flood of waters into the Gulf of Mexico, on the seventeenth of July Marquette and Joliet left Akansea, and ascended the Mississippi, having the greatest difficulty in stemming its currents.

At the thirty-eighth degree of latitude they entered the river Illinois, which was broad and deep and peaceful in its flow. Its banks were without a paragon for its prairies and its forests, its buffaloes and deer, its turkeys and geese, and many kinds of game, and even beavers ; and there were many small lakes and rivulets. "When I was told of a country without trees," wrote Joliet, "I imagined a country that had been burned over, or of a soil too poor to produce anything; but we have remarked just the contrary, and it would be impossible to find a better soil for grain, for vines, or any fruits whatever." He held the country on the Illinois River to be the most beautiful and the most easy to colonize. "There is no need," he said, "that an emigrant should employ ten years in cutting down the forest and burning it. On the day of his arrival the emigrant could put the plow into the earth." The tribe of the Illinois entreated Marquette to come and reside among them. One of their chiefs, with their young men, guided the party to the portage, which, in spring and the early part of summer, was but half a league long, and they easily reached the lake. "The place at which we entered the lake," to use the words of Joliet, "is a harbor very convenient to receive ships, and to give them protection against the wind." Before the end of September the explorers were safe in Green Bay ; but Marquette was exhausted by his labors.

In 1675, Marquette, who had been delayed by his failing health for more than a year, rejoined the Illinois on their river. Assembling the tribe, whose chiefs and

men were reckoned at two thousand, he raised before
them pictures of the Virgin Mary, spoke to them of
one who had died on the cross for all men, and built an
altar and said mass in their presence on the prairie.
Again celebrating the mystery of the Eucharist, on
Easter Sunday he took possession of the land in the
name of Jesus Christ, and there founded a mission.
This work being accomplished, his health failed him
and he began a journey through Chicago to Mackinaw.
On the way, feeling himself arrested by the approach
of death, he entered a little river in Michigan, and was
set on shore that he might breathe his last in peace.
He repeated in solitude all his acts of devotion of the
preceding days. When, after a little while his companions returned to him, they found him passing gently
away near the stream that has taken his name. On its
highest bank the canoemen dug his grave. To a city,
a county, and a river, Michigan has given his name.

———◆———

SONG OF THE CHATTAHOOCHEE

Sidney Lanier

Out of the hills of Habersham,
Down the valleys of Hall,
I hurry amain to reach the plain,
Run the rapid and leap the fall,
Split at the rock and together again,
Accept my bed, or narrow or wide,
And flee from folly on every side

With a lover's pain to attain the plain
    Far from the hills of Habersham,
    Far from the valleys of Hall.

    All down the hills of Habersham,
    All through the valleys of Hall,
The rushes cried, " Abide, abide,"
The willful waterweeds held me thrall,
The loving laurel turned my tide,
The ferns and the fondling grass said, " Stay,"
The dewberry dipped for to work delay,
And the little reeds sighed, " Abide, abide,"
    Here in the hills of Habersham,
    Here in the valleys of Hall.

    High o'er the hills of Habersham,
    Veiling the valleys of Hall,
The hickory told me manifold
Fair tales of shade ; the poplar tall
Wrought me her shadowy self to hold ;
The chestnut, the oak, the walnut, the pine,
Overleaning, with flickering meaning and sign,
Said : " Pass not so cold, these manifold
    Deep shades of the hills of Habersham,
    These glades in the valleys of Hall."

    And oft in the hills of Habersham,
    And oft in the valleys of Hall,
The white quartz shone, and the smooth brook stone
Did bar me of passage with friendly brawl ;
And many a luminous jewel lone

(Crystals clear or a-cloud with mist,
Ruby, garnet, or amethyst)
Made lures with the lights of streaming stone
    In the clefts of the hills of Habersham,
    In the beds of the valleys of Hall.

    But oh ! not the hills of Habersham,
    And oh ! not the valleys of Hall
Avail ; I am fain for to water the plain.
Downward the voices of Duty call ;
Downward to toil and be mixed with the main.
The dry fields burn, and the mills are to turn,
And a myriad flowers mortally yearn,
And the lordly main from beyond the plain
    Calls o'er the hills of Habersham,
    Calls through the valleys of Hall.

————♦————

JOHN BULL AND BROTHER JONATHAN

James Kirke Paulding

JOHN BULL was a choleric old fellow, who held a good manor in the middle of a great mill pond, and which, by reason of its being quite surrounded by water, was generally called " Bullock Island." Bull was an ingenious man, an exceedingly good blacksmith, a dexterous cutler, and a notable weaver besides. He was, in fact, a sort of Jack-at-all-trades, and good at each. In addition to these, he was a hearty fellow, a jolly companion, and passably honest, as the times go. But what tarnished all these qualities was an exceedingly quarrelsome, overbearing disposition, which was always getting him into some scrape or other. The truth is, he never heard of a quarrel going on among his neighbors but his fingers itched to take a part in it; so that he was hardly ever seen without an arm in a sling or a bruised eye. Such was Squire Bull, as he was commonly called by the country people, his neighbors — one of those odd, testy, grumbling, boasting old fellows that never get credit for what they are, because they are always pretending to be what they are not. The squire was as hard a hand to deal with indoors as out, sometimes treating his family as if they were not the same flesh and blood, when they happened to differ with him in certain matters.

One day he got into a dispute with his youngest son, Jonathan, who was familiarly called Brother Jonathan, whether churches ought to be called *churches* or *meeting-houses*, and whether steeples were not an abomination. The squire, either having the worst of the argument or being naturally impatient of contradiction — I can't tell which — fell into a great passion, and declared he would drive such notions out of the boy's head. So he went to some of his doctors, and had them draw up a prescription made of thirty-nine different articles, many of them bitter enough to some palates. This he tried to make Jonathan swallow; and, finding he made wry faces, and would not do it, fell upon him and beat him soundly. After this he made the house so disagreeable to him that Jonathan, though as hard as a pine knot and as tough as leather, could bear it no longer. Taking his gun and ax, he put himself into a boat and paddled over the mill pond to some new lands, to which the squire pretended to have some sort of claim. Jonathan intended to settle the lands, and build a meetinghouse without any steeple as soon as he grew rich enough.

When he got over, he found that the land was quite in a state of nature, covered with wood, and inhabited only by wild beasts. But, being a lad of spirit, he took his ax on one shoulder and his gun on the other, marched into the thickest of the wood, and clearing a place, built a log hut. Pursuing his labors, and handling his ax like an notable woodman, he in a few years cleared the land, which he laid out into *thirteen good farms;* and building himself a large house, which he partly furnished, began to be quite snug and comfortable.

But Squire Bull, who was getting old and stingy, and besides was in great want of money, on account of his having lately been made to pay heavy damages for assaulting his neighbors and breaking their heads — the squire, I say, finding Jonathan was getting well to do in the world, began to be very much troubled about his welfare; so he demanded that Jonathan should pay him a good rent for the land which he had cleared and made good for something. He made up I know not what claim against him, and under different pretenses managed to pocket all Jonathan's honest gains. In fact, the poor lad had not a shilling left for holiday was dining somewhere, the other guests found the oil too rancid for them. Cæsar took it without remark, to spare his entertainer's feeling. When on a journey through a forest with his friend Oppius, he came one night to a hut where there was a single bed. Oppius being unwell, Cæsar gave it up to him and slept on the ground.

Of Cæsar, too, it may be said that he came into the world at a special time and for a special object. The old religions were dead, from the pillars of Hercules to the Euphrates and the Nile, and the principles on which human society had been constructed were dead also. There remained of spiritual conviction only the common and human sense of justice and morality ; and out of this sense some ordered system of government had to be constructed, under which quiet men could live and labor and eat the fruit of their industry.

Under a rule of this material kind there can be no enthusiasm, no chivalry, no saintly aspirations, no patriotism of the heroic type. It was not to last forever. A new life was about to dawn for mankind. Poetry, and faith, and devotion, were to spring again out of the seeds which were sleeping in the heart of humanity.

But the life which is to endure grows slowly ; and as the soil must be prepared before the wheat can be sown, so before the kingdom of heaven could throw up its shoots there was needed a kingdom of this world where the nations were neither torn in pieces by violence, nor were rushing after false ideals and spurious ambitions.

Equal. Impartial.   **'Broidered, mellowed.** The same sunlight differently interpreted in its effect.   **Deed.** What deed?

THE DESTRUCTION OF SENNACHERIB

Sennacherib. See II Kings xix.   **As he passed.** Who passed?
Widows of Asshur. Asshur, the god of the Assyrians; and hence a general term for Assyrians.   **Baal.** An Assyrian deity.
Gentile. Any nations not Jewish.

A RUFFIAN IN FEATHERS

Man that hath no music. See *Merchant of Venice*, Act V., Scene i., — "The man that hath no music in himself," etc.
Bells jangled out of tune. See *Hamlet*, Act III., Scene i. — Ophelia's soliloquy over what she supposes is Hamlet's loss of reason.

THE RISING IN 1776

Out of the north. From Lexington, forty miles north of Berkeley Manor.   **Boreal.** A reference to the northern lights.
Baptismal name. She forgot the significance of the name her founders gave her: Concord = harmony.
Discord. In contrast with concord.
The lesson taught. What lesson?
Breathing. Exhaling the perfume of.
Renewed . . . attitude. Grown young and speaking eloquently by its very attitude.   **Dusty.** Why?

AN ORDER FOR A PICTURE

Gracious . . . down. Referring to the rich coloring of the clouds at sunset.   **Wilding.** Poetical word for wild.
Out in the field . . . day after day. While this stanza contains but one sentence, yet the pictures it presents are very clear and striking. By taking up each picture in succession, the complete conception may be easily grasped.
Notched . . . wool. Does this refer to the branch or to the leaves?

GRADATIM

Only . . . thrown. An allusion to Jacob's dream. See Genesis xxviii. 11–16.

UNDER THE GREENWOOD TREE

Who loves. By inserting *Let him* before these words, it will become clearer that they are the real subject of *come* in the fifth line.

TO DAFFODILS

Having pray'd together, *i.e.* the flowers and the writer.

HORSESHOE ROBINSON'S RUSE

Ninety Six. A village in South Carolina.
Ennoree. A river in South Carolina.
Tories. In this instance used to designate American sympathizers with England at the time of the Revolution.
Good lack! An exclamation of surprise.
Toping. Wine-drinking.
They . . . tavern. Observe the speaker's anger.
Suspicion. Incorrectly used for suspect, guess.
Scrummage. Provincial English for *scrimmage*.
Continental Congress. The congress of the revolting colonies.

ARNOLD VON WINKELRIED

At a critical moment in the great battle of Sempach (1386), which is a Swiss town in the canton of Lucerne, when the serried ranks of the Austrians seemed invulnerable, Arnold von Winkelried, a Swiss, commending his wife and children to the care of his comrades, rushed toward the Austrians, gathered a number of their spears together against his breast, and fell pierced through and through, thus making a way for his countrymen through what before was an unbroken line.

Human wood. The soldiers stood as thick and straight as trees in a forest. **Conscious.** Animate or intelligent.
Horrent. Bristling. **Along . . . sun.** The flashing crests of the waves as they roll toward the sun.
Hovering. Fluttering, moving to and fro irresolutely.
New-found. Found in recent insurrection against their masters.
And what . . . maintained. See preceding note on *new-found*.
Tell. The Swiss hero, who defied the Austrian tyrant, Gessler.
Switzers. Another form of the word *Swiss*.

An immortal date. The victory of Sempach in 1386, henceforth to be ever remembered by the Swiss and the world.

As 'twere a secret known. Without expressing the thought.

That one . . . alone. That upon one man might depend the victory.

THE SPANIARDS' RETREAT FROM MEXICO

Hernando Cortés (1485–1547), a Spaniard, served as a high official in the island of Cuba, under Velasquez, and later was sent to conquer Mexico, which had only recently been discovered. He set sail, in November, 1518, with ten vessels, about seven hundred Spaniards, and a few pieces of cannon, and landed in Mexico in March of 1519. Cortés learned that the native sovereign was called Montezuma, and that he reigned over an extensive empire, and was possessed of immense wealth. This information determined Cortés to undertake the conquest of the empire. He first conquered Tlascala, and converted the people into powerful auxiliaries. He then proceeded to Mexico, where he made Montezuma a prisoner. Here he remained for several months. At last, driven to desperation, the Aztecs, who were the native inhabitants, drove the Spaniards from Mexico. The beginning of the retreat is described in the present selection.

Tlascala. A small republic near the city of Mexico.

Causeway of Tlacopan. A roadway connecting the city of Mexico, which was surrounded by water, with the mainland. The causeway was intersected by canals spanned by wooden bridges. These the Aztecs had destroyed to prevent the escape of the Spaniards.

The royal fifth. The portion of the booty that went to the Crown.

Castilian. From Castile in Spain.   **Teocallis.** Aztec temples.

Mêlée (*Mā-lā'*). A hand-to-hand conflict.

THE SCHOOL AT DOTHEBOYS HALL

Was making his fortune. How was he making his fortune?

A pretty go. A fine condition of affairs; used ironically.

Consort. Wife; here used to give a mock dignity to the description.   **Treacle.** A kind of sirup.

Fustian. Corduroy, velveteen.   **Treacled.** There is no such word. The term is of course used humorously.

Not remarking the emphasis. What was this emphasis, and what did it imply?   **Coppers.** Copper boilers.

THE BURIAL OF MOSES

Nebo's lonely mountain. Nebo is east of the river Jordan, opposite the northern end of the Dead Sea.

And . . . sepulcher. See the last chapter of Deuteronomy.

Noiselessly. It will help the reading of this and the following stanza to notice that *noiselessly* is to be connected in sense with *swept*.

Beth-peor. Moses was supposed to be buried in a valley near Beth-peor, in the land of Moab, east of the Jordan.

Minster transept. *Minster*, originally the church of a monastery; now applied to any large church. *Transept*, that portion of the church which crosses its greatest length at right angles, and is between the nave and the choir. In Gothic churches, the projecting parts of the transept are called the arms.

THE DISCOVERY OF THE MISSISSIPPI

The Mississippi was discovered by De Soto, in the spring of 1542. The present extract deals with the discovery of the northern portion of the river.

Frontenac. See *The Heroine of Verchères* (Indiana Fourth Reader).

Pottawatomies. A tribe of friendly Indians.

Great River. The Mississippi; so called by the Indians.

Alloüez. A French missionary, who lived among the Indians.

Manitou. Indian name for God.

Algonquins. A general term, including nearly all the tribes mentioned in this extract.

Published. Announced, preached of.

Five Nations. Another name for the Iroquois, a confederation of tribes, including the Mohawks, Oneidas, Onondagas, Cayugas, and Senecas. **Calumet.** Peace pipe.

Eucharist. The sacrament of the Lord's Supper.

SONG OF THE CHATTAHOOCHEE

Notice how the joy of the river finds expression in the movement of the rhythm.

Chattahoochee. A river in Georgia.

Habersham and **Hall.** Two counties in northeastern Georgia.

Amain. With all my might. **Thrall.** In bondage.

Fondling. Caressing.

The hickory . . . sign. Referring to the shadows of the trees and leaves in the water.

Flickering. Why *flickering?*

Streaming stone. The light streaming from the stone. See *luminous* in the same stanza.

JOHN BULL AND BROTHER JONATHAN

It is hardly necessary to remark that this selection deals with the revolt of the American colonies against England. Many passages otherwise meaningless present no difficulty when we grasp the main idea of the narrative.

Good . . . besides. Referring to England's large iron, cutlery, and wool industries.

A dispute . . . son. Referring to the Puritans.

Doctors. Of theology.

Thirty-nine articles. Articles of faith in the English church.

Thirteen good farms. The thirteen colonies.

Linsey-woolsey. Cloth made of linen and wool, mixed.

THE BUILDING OF THE SHIP

Master. Head of the shipyard.

The heir of his dexterity. To succeed him as a master shipbuilder.

Scarfed. Scarf joint, a joint made by overlapping and bolting together the ends of two pieces of timber that are notched, or cut away, so that they will fit each other and form a lengthened beam of the same size at the junction as elsewhere.

Blocks. Ships are generally built on blocks, which are laid on an incline, for facility in launching.

Slip. An inclined plane on which a vessel is built.

Stemson. A piece of curved timber bolted to the stem and keelson in a ship's frame near the bow.

Keelson. A piece of timber laid on the middle of the floor timbers over the keel, and binding the floor timbers to the keel.

Sternson knee. The end of a ship's keelson, to which the sternpost is bolted. Hence the line indicates the general outline of the ship's skeleton.

Sheathing. The covering of a ship's bottom and sides.

Shrouds. A set of ropes serving as stays to support the mast.

Dight. Dressed, clad.

Brazen ring. In which the compass swings free, and so maintains its level.

Fortunate Isles. "Islands of the Blessed." In the Greek conception these were the happy abodes of the immortal heroes.

Shores. Props, to support the ship before launching.

Spurs. Pieces of timber attached to the bottom of the ship to hold it in position before launching.

JULIUS CÆSAR

Pillars of Hercules. A name given by the ancients to the Rock of Gibraltar and the opposite mountain, Jebel Zatout.

Sanhedrim. The great council of the Jews.

Cicero. A great Roman orator of the time of Cæsar.

Te Deums. Te Deum laudamus (We praise thee, O God!) are the first three words of the psalm of praise. Hence this psalm is called a *Te Deum*.

A PSALM OF LIFE

While this poem is apparently simple, and usually found in third and fourth readers, its reflections on life and its deeper meaning do not belong to the ordinary feelings of younger readers; and it is therefore reserved for its present place.

Muffled drums. Referring to the military custom of deadening the sound of the drum at the burial of soldiers.

Bivouac. The watch of a whole army by night, when in danger of surprise or attack.

UNION AND LIBERTY

Wide beams. United rays of all the stars upon the banner.

Of Liberty's van. Of the nation that is in the vanguard of liberty.

Many in one. A translation of the Latin *e pluribus unum*, the motto of the United States.

THE EAGLE'S NEST

Tree gnomons. A gnomon is a stick which by its shadow shows the time of day. Hence, a tree gnomon is a tree that serves the purpose of such a stick. **Bullion bars.** Why bullion?

O' ony puir. Of any poor. **Wean.** A young child.

Bairn. Scotch word for child. **Strath.** A valley.

Top-gallant sail. The sail near the top of the mast.

Kirk. Church.   **Claes.** Clothes.

Bonnie bit. Sweet little.   **Nane.** None.

Na. Not.   **Wauken.** Awake.

Maun hae. Must have.   **Wark.** Work.

RING OUT, WILD BELLS

Fuller minstrel. A poet who can look at life more hopefully and with a wider view.

Civic . . . spite. Referring to the bitterness and misrepresentations of political life.

The thousand years of peace. See Revelation xx.

THE SOLITARY REAPER

This little poem has the quaint simplicity and yet the depth of feeling characteristic of much of Wordsworth's poetry. The theme is as simple as its treatment, and this illustrates Wordsworth's theory that a poetic light should be thrown around common things.

Arabian sands. How does the addition of these words heighten the effect of the comparison?

Farthest Hebrides. Why are these words added to the comparison?

Plaintive numbers. A song expressive of sorrow or melancholy.

Far-off things. Distant events. Note the contrast between *old, far-off,* and *familiar matter of to-day.* The close of the last stanza and all of the second are especially rich in melody.

THE CHARACTER OF WASHINGTON

Newton, Bacon, Locke. Great English philosophers.

FITZ–JAMES AND RODERICK DHU

Though space . . . slain. Roderick refers to the sportsman's spirit of giving noble game a chance for its life; and for the moment, thinking Fitz-James a spy, compares him to a prowling fox, that would naturally be denied such a privilege.

They do. *Do* is emphatic.

Come. What does the absence of the comma after this word signify?

Glaive. A sword.   **Targe.** A shield.

Jack. A coarse, leather coat of defense.

Lay. Depended the possession of.

Carpet knight. A knight who enjoys ease and security and has not known the hardships of the field.

A VISIT TO NIAGARA

Fancy . . . Now, really! Have the student conceive the mood in which these words were uttered, and note if he gets the inflection described in the text.

Herdbook. A record of the pedigree of cattle in important herds.

Newport. A fashionable summer resort. Observe the irony.

"Saturday Review." An important English periodical.

The clamor of hackmen. At one time the hackmen rendered a visit to Niagara exceedingly disagreeable by their persistent endeavors to persuade the tourist to engage their services.

Goat Island. A small island just above the Falls.

Prospect Park. A park overlooking the rapids below the Falls.

American Fall. The Niagara River is divided by Goat Island into two parts, each of which descends into the abyss below, one known as the American Fall, the other as the Canadian (Horseshoe) Fall.

Clifton House. A hotel at Clifton, on the Canadian side of the river.

On the foam-crested river. Below the falls. Why foam-crested?

BATTLE HYMN OF THE REPUBLIC

Trampling out the vintage. A reference to the primitive custom of pressing the juice from the grapes by human feet.

Altar. The consecration of the soldiers at evening to the cause of freedom and God.

His righteous sentence. His judgment against slavery. In what can it be *read?*

Burnished rows of steel. The bayonets, which seem to say what follows in the next two lines.

Let the Hero . . . heel. See Genesis iii. 15.

Sifting out. To find the true and brave who are ready to sacrifice themselves for His cause.

With a glory . . . me. With a spirit of self-sacrifice that can transform each of us, if it takes possession of our lives.

Especial attention should be given to bringing out in the reading the magnificent marching rhythm of this stirring battle hymn.

O CAPTAIN! MY CAPTAIN!

This beautiful and heartfelt tribute to President Lincoln is especially appropriate, as Mr. Whitman was his personal friend and served with remarkable loyalty and tenderness as a hospital nurse during the Civil War. Lincoln is represented as in command of the ship of state.

Fearful trip. The course of the nation through the perils of civil war. **Rack.** Storm or tempest.

The prize we sought. Victory and the freedom of the slave.

Exult, O shores. Note the strong contrast between the exultant joy of the shores and bells, on the one hand, and on the other the poet's own lonely personal sorrow for his dead leader.

SPEECH ON A RESOLUTION TO PUT VIRGINIA INTO A STATE OF DEFENSE

In 1774 Patrick Henry, a lawyer and statesman of Virginia, was chosen a delegate to the Virginia convention. In the following year, he delivered a remarkable speech in moving that the "colony be immediately put in a state of defense" against England, and at the head of a body of militia he forced the royal officials to pay £330 for powder clandestinely removed by order of the English governor, Dunmore. He was later elected the first republican governor of Virginia, and several times reëlected.

Already in the field. Against England at the opening of the Revolutionary War.

THE DAY IS DONE

A feeling . . . rain. A sad experience that children are not likely to have had, — a sense of the pathos and loneliness of the on-coming night.

Not . . . endeavor. The truth of this may be illustrated by the teacher's reading selections from Milton, Shakespeare, and other "bards sublime." **Who.** What is the antecedent?

RAB AND HIS FRIENDS

Old Isaac. Isaac Watts, who wrote the poem containing the lines, "Let dogs delight to bark and bite," etc.

Facer. A blow in the face. **Buck.** A dandy, a fop.

Mull. A snuff box, made from the small end of a horn.

Cullō'den. In Scotland where was fought a great battle in 1746.

Shakespearean dewlaps. *Dewlap*, the pendulous skin under the neck of an ox, which laps the dew in grazing. Shakespeare, in *A Midsummer Night's Dream*, compares the hounds of Theseus, with reference to their dewlaps, to Thessalian bulls.

Black-a-vised. With a dark complexion.

Homer. The Greek poet, to whom tradition attributes the Iliad and the Odyssey.

Sir Walter. Scott. **Rehearse.** Relate. **Puir.** Poor.

Trojans. That is, in sympathy with the Trojans.

Hector. The Trojan hero, killed by Achilles before Troy.

Spartan. Spartans were famous for their brevity of speech.

Boo. Bow. **Breest.** Breast.

Income. An internal growth, as a cancer or tumor.

Plaid. A plaid shawl.

Mutch. A provincial term for a cap of linen worn by old women.

Freend. Friend.

Ye ken. A common term in Scotland, meaning you know.

Aboot. About. **Wull.** Will. **Bide.** Remain.

I'se warrant he's do that. I'll guarantee he will do that.

Archbishop Leighton's father. Who was tortured for his religious independence in the reign of Charles I.

Glower. Scowl. **Hap.** To wrap. **Tacket.** A Scotch word for a small broad-headed nail. **Nane.** None. **Gang.** Go.

Canny. Slyly, softly. **Snell.** Archaic term for nimble, quick.

Semper paratus. Always ready.

Fremyt. Probably akin to *fremd*, an old Scotch term meaning far off, or unusual.

Ma ain bonnie wee dawtie. My own pretty little girl.

Animula blandula, vagula, hospes, comesque. Sweet, fleeting little soul, guest-friend and companion.

Wae. Woe. **Bairn.** Child. **Mair.** More. **Clean silly.** Completely out of her mind.

In statu quo. Just where he had been before.

Lave. Scotch term meaning the remainder, the others.

Sorted. Carefully arranged her garments.

There was nae doin' wi him. There was no doing with him; that is, we could do nothing with him.

Treviss. Manger. **Mear.** Mare. **Wadna.** Would not.

Tempet. Tempted. **Kail.** Broth. **Naething.** Nothing.

Keepit. Kept. **Frae.** From.

Gur, gurrin'. Growling.

Grup, gruppin'. To grab with the mouth and growl.

Laith. Loath, unwilling. **Auld.** Old. **Wasna.** Was not.

THE CROWDED STREET

How slow the light. How slow the morning is in coming.
There is who heeds. Supply *one* after *is;* hence, the emphasis
will fall on *is.*

THE ARSENAL AT SPRINGFIELD

The effectiveness of this noble poem will be much increased by
keeping before the pupil's mind the imagery of the organ that runs
all through the poem.

Death angel. Why is the death angel conceived as playing this
great organ?

Miserere (*Miz-e-rē'rè*). A Latin word, meaning have mercy; it is
the opening word in the Latin version of the 50th Psalm, the
psalm of penitence.

Symphonies. Harmonies. **Harness.** Armor.

Hammer. War-club.

Cimbric forest. The woods of the Cimbri, an ancient tribe of
northern Germany.

Norseman. One of the ancient Scandinavians.

Tartar gong. An instrument, first used in the East, made of an
alloy of copper and tin, shaped like a disk, and producing,
when struck, a harsh and resounding noise. Used by the
Tartars as a signal for war.

Aztec. One of the early races of Mexico at the time of the Spanish
conquest, in 1519.

Teocallis. Singular *teocal'li*, Mexican, meaning God's house; temple,
usually of pyramidal form, such as were built by the aborigines
of Mexico and Yucatan.

Diapason. One of certain stops in an organ, so called because
they extend through the scale of the instrument; in this case,
the full power of the organ. The use of this word here illustrates how the organ metaphor pervades the poem.

THE SHELL

Spine, whorl. The back and curl of the shell.

Diamond . . . frill. Referring to the play of the sunlight on the
water.

The three-decker's oaken spine. Note the poetic comparison of
the strength of the three-decker with that of the delicate shell.

IN FAVOR OF INDEPENDENCE

Are not you, sir. Addressed to the chairman, John Hancock, upon whose head England had placed a price.

Boston Port Bill. An act passed by the British Parliament (1774) to shut up the port of Boston until the people of that city should be starved or frightened into paying for the tea destroyed by the Boston Tea Party.

THE *REVENGE*

Inquisition dogs. The Spaniards, whose persecutions during the time of the Inquisition had made them hated and feared.

For the glory of the Lord. Notice the strain of sarcasm in these closing words of the stanza.

Weather bow. Bow toward the wind; opposed to *lee.*

Sĕ'ville. A Spanish city that here represents the whole of Spain.

Grisly. Frightful, ghastly. **Or ever.** Before ever.

THE BATTLE OF WATERLOO

Austerlitz. The famous battle of 1805, when Napoleon and the French overthrew the Austrians.

Blücher. The Prussian general who coöperated with the Duke of Wellington in the battle.

How much . . . sea. A clear idea of the geography here will be of great advantage to the pupil.

Those who . . . there. The imagination of the child should here be helped by a simple diagram on the blackboard.

Hougoumont . . . La Haie Sainte. Both of these strategic points had fallen into the possession of the French.

Talavera, Vittoria, and Salamanca. Cities in Spain, which gave their names to great victories won over the French by the English during the Peninsular War.

Cressy, Poitiers, Malplaquet, and Ramillies. Famous victories of the English over the French.

The man of Marengo. Napoleon, who won one of his most brilliant victories over the Austrians at Marengo, May, 1800.

Agincourt. The famous victory of King Henry V. of England over the French in 1415.

Vive l'Empereur. Long live the Emperor.

Debouched. To march out from a wood, defile, or other confined spot, into open ground; to issue.

Hanoverian. Hanover, a province of Prussia.

Guard. The "Old Guard" were the veteran soldiers of Napoleon, on whom he most relied and whose greatest ambition was to fight and die for him.

Twenty victories . . . extended. A reference to the "large eagle plates" of the guards, just mentioned, and also to the classical conception of personified Victory flying over the battlefield.

Sauve qui peut. Let every one save himself that can.

THE VILLAGE PREACHER

Copse. A wood of small growth; a thicket of brushwood.

A few . . . disclose. How do they disclose it?

Passing. Surprisingly, exceedingly.

By . . . hour. By means of doctrines formulated to meet the changing views of the hour.

Kindred. Recognition as a brother or friend in need of sympathy.

His pity . . . began. He instinctively showed his loving sympathy and compassion, without the thought of making allowance for defects or vices.

Reproved . . . delay. Reproved their lack of effort toward the good. In contrast with the preceding thought of his using every art of allurement. **Dismayed.** Whom?

At his control. Through his efforts of sympathy and prayer.

His lips. The emphasis is to be placed on *his* and *double*.

As . . . head. In this remarkable simile, what is the point of resemblance to the village preacher?

RUTH

Beth-lehem-judah. *I.e.* Bethlehem in the land of Judah, to distinguish it from other Bethlehems.

Moab. Near Judah to the east. The religion of the inhabitants was different from that of the other Jews, and of a degraded kind.

Left. Bereft.

In the house of her husband. *I.e.* of another husband. "The times were rude and wild. A woman could be safe and respected only under the protection of her husband. Not only was there the old-world contempt for unmarried women, but, we may say, they were an impossibility; there was no place for them in the social life."

Turn again, my daughters. Naomi wishes them to understand
that if they go with her to Judah, their lot may prove a hard
one; they arè strangers, penniless, and of a different language
and religion.

Moved about. Deeply interested in the arrival of.

Naomi, Mara. The former means, *God is sweet;* the latter, *bitter.*

Let me now . . . find grace. The Israelites allowed the poor the
privilege of gleaning after the reapers. In spite of the humil-
iation that would follow such a step, Ruth, to meet the needs
of Naomi and herself, asks for the privilege.

Hap. Fortune, lot.

The Lord be with you. The usual Oriental salutation.

That . . . house. Ruth was so eager to glean, that she took but
little rest.

Then . . . face. A common Oriental custom in the presence of a
superior. **Vinegar.** Sour wine, a very common beverage
with outdoor workers.

Ephah. A Hebrew measure equal to about half a bushel.

Rest. A husband and home.

Floor. At time of harvest it was common for the owner of the
grain to sleep on the threshing-floor.

And it shall be . . . and lay thee down. " Naomi ventured on a
bold expedient to bring speedy 'rest' to her daughter-in-law.
But we assume that, with unmistaking feminine intuition, she
saw, on the one hand, that Boaz was already deeply attached
to Ruth, and on the other that Ruth reciprocated his attach-
ment with pure intensity. He had unconsciously revealed
himself, and made it clear to Naomi that he wished to divulge
in words the depth of his honorable feelings. The scheme of
Naomi would have been imprudent and improper and utterly
unfeminine, had it not been the case that, in virtue of an
ancient and much-prized Jewish law, Ruth was entitled to call
upon her nearest of kin to fulfill the various duties of a responsible kinsman." Boaz, as Naomi has said, was "one of our
next kinsmen."

Mark the place. Notice or observe the place.

Vail. A sort of shawl; not the modern veil.

The gate. The city gate, the natural meeting place in an Oriental
city, corresponding to the forum or market place of a Western
city. Boaz would naturally expect his kinsman to pass out to
his fields, or back from his threshing-floor through the one
gate of the city.

Brother Elimelech. *Brother* in the sense of near kinsman.

Advertise. To give notice to.

After thee. Next in order of kinship.

Thou must buy it also . . . inheritance. "Boaz distinctly informed his relative that if the land was acquired at all by a kinsman, it must be acquired with its living appurtenance, Ruth the Moabitess, so that, by the blessing of God, the fountain of families, there might be the opportunity of retaining the possession of the property in the line of her deceased husband, that line coalescing in the line of her second husband. It was the pleasure of Naomi and Ruth, in offering their property for sale, to burden its acquisition, on the part of a kinsman, with the condition specified. If there should be fruit after the marriage, the child would be heir of the property, just as if he had been Mahlon's son, even though the father should have other and older sons by another wife."

Shoe. To symbolize that he freely gave up his right to walk upon the soil, in favor of the person who had acquired the possession.

To raise up the name of the dead upon his inheritance. That his kinsmen Elimelech and Mahlon might have a direct heir through the marriage of Ruth and himself.

Pharez. Pharez's descendants were particularly numerous. See Num. xxvi. 20, 21.

This day. The day of the child's birth.

A kinsman. Ruth's son.

THE FORUM SCENE FROM JULIUS CAESAR

It will require but a few minutes to place before the pupils the events in the drama that lead up to the present scene.

Give me audience. Give me a hearing.

Part the numbers. Divide the crowd. The two lines beginning, "Cassius, go you," etc., are, no doubt, uttered as an aside.

Be patient to the last. For suggestive remarks on this speech, see *Julius Cæsar*, Rolfe edition, p. 163 *et seq*.

Censure. Not in the modern sense, but here meaning to judge.

The question of his death. The explanation of our course in killing Cæsar. The answer to the question why we killed him.

Enrolled. Recorded. **Extenuated.** Underestimated.

Enforced. Exaggerated.

Wasteful. Waste, desolate, unoccupied.

Alexanders. Alexander the Great wept for more worlds to conquer. **Lack of argument.** Lack of an opportunity or cause.

Now attest . . . you. Now prove that you really are the sons of your noble fathers.

Copy. Pattern, model. **Of grosser blood.** Of lower rank.

Yeomen. The king has previously been addressing the officers and nobility in his army; now, the rank and file.

Mettle of your pasture. The spirit that should come from your rearing in England.

Mean and base. Of humble birth, in contrast with noble or aristocratic. **Noble luster.** The spirit of the highborn.

In the slips. In the leash, by which a dog is restrained.

Harry . . . Saint George. *Harry*, Henry V.; *Saint George*, the patron saint of England. The legendary St. George killed a dragon in Libya and rescued the princess Sabra, as related in a ballad found in Percy's *Reliques*.

The spirit of the poem may be easily grasped when the child has once perceived the meaning of the words; and the labor of acquiring this mastery is quickly forgotten in the added zest of enjoyment. The imaginative element in this selection appeals with striking force to the pupil, and will prove a strong stimulant to vigorous vocal expression.

ELEGY IN A COUNTRY CHURCHYARD

" The poem opens with a description of the churchyard and its surroundings as they appear in the mellow shades of twilight. The grassy mounds of the graveyard lead the poet to meditate on the life and fate of its humble occupants. He recounts their cares, their labors, and their joys, and then calls upon the great of the earth not to despise the simple story of the poor, bidding them remember that death comes alike to all, and that their posthumous honors can as little recall them to life, as these 'neglected' graves can reanimate the poor. He continues to reflect how circumstances alone prevented them from attaining the positions and wielding the influence for which their natural abilities fitted them; how, likewise, their lot prevented them from committing the crimes and follies of those in higher spheres of life. But even they have not passed away unremembered, for these 'frail memorials' perpetuate their memory while instructing future generations. This reminds